Investment appraisal
in forestry
with particular reference to conifers in Britain

by R J N Busby and A J Grayson   *Forestry Commission*

London: Her Majesty's Stationery Office.

ODC No. 651:652:67

Enquiries relating to this publication
should be addressed to the Publications
Officer, Forestry Commission Research
Station, Alice Holt Lodge, Wrecclesham,
Farnham, Surrey, GU10 4LH.

ISBN 0 11 710190 7

Printed in England for Her Majesty's Stationery Office
by Hobbs the Printers of Southampton
(1638) Dd0696970 K24 3/81 G327

Contents

Appendices

Summary

The purpose of investment appraisal is to show the relative profitability of alternative courses of action. The measure of profit used is net discounted revenue at a chosen discount rate. Attention is concentrated on conifers in pure stands. The assumptions adopted in preparing tables of discounted revenue at 3, 5 and 7% are the predictions of Forestry Commission yield tables. A generalised curve relating standing tree values with diameter at breast height is assumed. Discounted revenues for the major conifer species by yield classes are tabulated in the appendices. Illustrative examples of their use are presented for appraisal of land purchase, choice of species, fertilisation, beating up, weeding and cleaning, crop protection, roading, thinning, timing of felling and crop replacement. Taxes and grants often affect costs and returns to the private or corporate owner and thus influence commercial decisions which should be based on post-tax and post-grant costs and revenues.

Acknowledgements

The authors wish to acknowledge the help given by colleagues in both the Forestry Commission and private forestry who suggested many improvements to an early draft of the text.

Thanks are also due to past and present members of the Planning and Economics Division of the Forestry Commission, whose work has been used as the basis for some of the sections in this Booklet, and in particular to Jim Dewar, Mike Garforth and John Morgan; and especially to Bob Cochrane who carried out all the programming and computer work.

I. The Principles of Investment Appraisal

Introduction

The purposes of this Booklet are to outline the basic concepts of investment appraisal as they apply to forestry, to provide tables of use in appraisal and to illustrate their application to a variety of cases in forestry.

The Appendices and Tables relate only to the common conifers. Broadleaves have not been covered owing to the difficulty of nominating plausible and generally acceptable assumptions on the value of broadleaved trees of different sizes. Their exclusion should not be taken to imply that management of broadleaved woodlands does not merit the same treatment of appraising options as arises with conifers. Indeed, the range of options may well be wider. As with commercial coniferous woodlands, the purpose of appraisal may not be simply to discover the course of action likely to yield the highest profit but rather to determine the cost of departing from it in order to satisfy some non-commercial objective.

The economic justification of a project lies in the belief that the cost of carrying out the project will be more than covered by the income generated by it. Where there is a significant lapse of time between the start of costs being incurred and the end of the period in which all costs and benefits arise the original expenditure is considered to be an *investment*. An investment is thus any action which incurs costs now and gives returns in the future.

Because of the time lag between incurring costs and receiving returns, especially in forestry, it is not always easy to evaluate the costs and returns. In particular, difficulties arise in predicting future inputs and outputs in physical terms (e.g. man-hours, cubic metres), assessing the future value of these inputs and outputs and comparing the value of the costs and returns arising at different times. Because of these difficulties it is often not immediately apparent that a particular investment is worth doing or which is the best investment to choose from among several alternatives. This is, however, no excuse for not attempting to make any appraisal of the investment but emphasises the need for such appraisals rather than relying on intuition.

Discounting

Investment appraisal entails quantifying future costs and returns, evaluating in terms of a common measure, namely £s, and weighting these values to take account of their timing by the process of discounting. The concept of discounting for time is based on the premise that, in general, people prefer to receive benefits sooner rather than later. If offered £1 now or in a year's time (and leaving aside at this stage the question of inflation) most people would have it now. If they have it now they can either buy some goods which bring them current satisfaction or they can invest the money so that at the end of, say, one year it brings returns in excess of the original amount invested. Thus £1 received now is considered by most people to be of greater value than £1 at some future date. Just how much depends on the individual's attitude to time. Some people may value £110 next year as equivalent to £100 now, while others may value £105 as equivalent.

Just as compound interest is applied to show how an investment grows to some point in the future, so one can discount in order to bring some future amount back to the present. As a matter of convention it is usually assumed that the discount rate remains constant through time. By this means all costs and returns can be increased or decreased by a set factor each year in order to make them comparable with other costs and returns which arise at different points in time. Where values are increased to make them comparable with a value at a later date, this is known as *compounding* and when values are reduced to make them comparable with values at an earlier date this is known as *discounting*. The compounding and discounting formulae and factors for a range of rates are shown in Appendix 1. The following examples illustrate the calculation of the *present value* (that is the value discounted or compounded to the present) of various sums:

		5% compound or discount factor	Present value at 5%, £
£70	4 years ago	1.216	85.1
£100	now	1.0	100.0
£250	in 10 years	0.614	153.5
£500	in 15 years	0.481	240.5

The terms *discounted expenditure* and *discounted revenue* relate to the present values of either individual sums of money or sets of sums expended or received. Thus the discounted revenue at 5% from revenues of £250 received 10 years hence and £500 received 15 years hence equals £153.5 plus £240.5, or £394.0. *Net discounted revenue* (NDR) is equal to the difference between discounted revenue (DR) and discounted expenditure (DE). If the DR for a particular project is estimated at £160 and the DE at £100 the NDR is £60. The common point to which all *cash flows* are usually related is either the present or the starting year of the investment under consideration. Once all cash flows have been brought to the same point in time it is possible to rank them in order of present value and identify the one with the highest net present value (i.e. NDR).

The Measurement of Relevant Costs and Returns

The first question that arises is which costs and revenues are to be included in an investment appraisal. Where an item of revenue or expenditure in a particular year remains the same whether or not the investment is undertaken, such an item may be omitted from the appraisal. For instance, there are costs associated with an enterprise which are unlikely to change whether a particular investment is undertaken or not. Examples of this might arise in appraising a fertiliser programme for a forest. Some foresters' time will be involved in the operation but it is unlikely that there will be any additional payment of salaries as a result of going ahead with the programme or any reduction in the total salary bill if the programme is not undertaken. In such circumstances these costs are therefore *fixed costs* which do not vary with the investment and thus can be excluded from the appraisal. Most overhead costs come into this category although some costs which are often considered as overheads, such as labour oncost (wet time, holidays, travelling etc.) are usually not independent of the investment and so need to be taken into account.

In contrast to fixed costs are the *variable costs*. These do need to be considered in an appraisal because the costs will vary depending on whether the investment is undertaken or not. There is no sharp dividing line between fixed costs and variable costs but the further into the future a cost is incurred the more likely it is to be variable.

A similar sort of consideration arises where an appraisal is being made of an investment in harvesting roads in an area due for first thinning and there is an existing pre-planting road. In these circumstances, the original cost of the pre-planting road can be ignored as the money has already been spent and will be unaffected by any decision regarding the harvesting roads.

Inflation

It might be thought that future inflation must cause difficulties in estimating future costs and returns. In practice, the inclusion of an assumption about future inflation is relevant only where loans are concerned and repayment is due in money regardless of how the purchasing power of the £ has changed over time. Otherwise the best way to handle inflation expected in the future is to ignore it. By removing the effects of inflation one deals with values expressed in *real terms*. This does not mean, however, that one necessarily assumes that all costs and prices will move in harmony in the future. The prices of some goods and services will rise relative to others, that is they show an increase in *relative* (or *real*) price. If they do the relative price of others must fall. For example, it is likely that with increased standards of living real earnings and the price of services, for example haircuts, will rise while the real price of most manufactured goods may fall.

Such trends in real price, if confidently predicted, should be included in any appraisal. This can most simply be done by converting the trend in real costs or prices into a compound interest percentage and then discounting. For example, suppose that the chosen discount rate is 5% but that there is good evidence to suggest that prices are going to *increase* in real terms, i.e. relative to other goods and services, at 2% per annum. In this case, the costs will continue to be discounted at 5% but the prices will rise at 2% and then be discounted at 5%. This means that prices unadjusted for their predicted real increase can be discounted at 3% (5% − 2%), the approximation being satisfactory for most purposes at low rates of interest, to find their present value in real terms.

Non-Market Costs and Benefits

The money values of costs and revenues based directly on market measures may not always reflect the *social costs and benefits* of a particular investment. Differences between market and social values may arise because resources may be priced above or below their real value to society, or because there is no market in goods and services produced or consumed, for example landscape or clean water.

4

Normally *cost-benefit analysis* incorporating measures in social terms of the various inputs and outputs is undertaken by Government bodies, but not by private owners. There may, of course, be non-market costs or benefits of a course of action taken by a private owner either to himself or to his heirs (e.g. gain in amenity) but, in this case, the owner himself is in the best position to make a subjective choice having considered the results of the financial appraisal.

Choice of Discount Rate

The level of the discount rate is of paramount importance in forestry owing to the large effects a small change in rate has when used to discount values over long periods of time. The discount rate used in the public sector generally is related to the rate of return on capital in the private sector of the industry and commerce. The test discount rate is currently set at a minimum of 5% applied to costs and returns expressed in real terms (Cmnd 7131 April 1978 and Hansard, House of Commons, 5 April 1978).

However, the economic environment of the private sector differs from that in the public sector, for example because of taxes or different valuations of non-market costs and benefits, and as a result there will be differences in discount rate. In this account, discount rates of 3, 5 and 7% have been employed in an attempt to cover the range of real rates of return likely to be available from alternative investments open to private investors in forestry. Where an investor is uncertain which rate is most appropriate in his circumstances, he can separately discount his cash flows at each of these rates and thereby determine the internal rate of return (the rate at which NDR is zero) by either interpolation or extrapolation. An example of this calculation is given on pages 17 and 18. The investor must then decide whether he considers this rate of return to be satisfactory.

Risk, Uncertainty and Sensitivity Analysis

Uncertainty obviously has a bearing when considering future events. Very often in investment appraisal it is assumed that cash flows can be predicted with certainty. Where there are a number of possible outcomes resulting from an investment it may be possible to measure the *risk* involved by considering what has happened in the past. It may then be possible to allocate probabilities to each possible outcome. For example, it may be estimated that on average over the long-term there is a 30 per cent (i.e. 0.3) chance that a crop will be blown down when it reaches a top height of 16 m, a 40 per cent chance of this happening at 17 m and a 30 per cent chance of it remaining until the designated height of felling of 18 m. The DR for each event is multiplied by its probability and the sum of the products used as the expected DR having taken into account the risk (note that the probabilities of all possible events must sum to unity):

Expected DR = 0.3 (DR: 16 m) + 0.4 (DR: 17 m) + 0.3 (DR: 18 m)

Very often in forestry such probabilities will have to be estimated subjectively.

Whether or not it is possible to assign probabilities to different outcomes it may well be useful to carry out a *sensitivity analysis*. This looks at the variation in the results of an appraisal when some of the assumptions are changed. Sensitivity analysis, as its name implies, indicates to which assumption the results are most sensitive. For example, it may be helpful to show the consequences of a particular course of action in terms of net discounted revenue at a variety of discount rates indicating the sensitivity of the results to the choice of discount rate.

In the absence of any guidance on the likely range of values of the various factors the analysis has to be conducted on the basis of determining the sensitivity of the results to a given percentage change (say 10 per cent) in each of the factors. Examples of sensitivity analysis are given on pages 18 and 21.

II. The Assumptions

Revenues

The forest yields a number of benefits in addition to timber. Some have a market value, such as sporting lettings, while others such as amenity and conservation are more difficult, if not impossible, to value in money terms. In this account we shall only be considering the revenues derived from the yield of wood. If there are additional sources of money income which can be foreseen, for example the sale of foliage and sporting rentals, these should be included.

Yields

The yield data used in computing the tables and appendices that are given in this Booklet are based on those given in the metric version of the *Forest Management Tables* (Hamilton and Christie, 1971) and on more recent work carried out by the Commission's Mensuration Section, such as that described in the Bulletin entitled *Influence of Spacing on Crop Characteristics and Yield*, also by Hamilton and Christie (1974).

British yield tables have related to pure even-aged crops only, but if tables for mixtures or uneven-aged stands were available there would be no difference in the principles of conversion from yield to discounted revenue. Yield models being published by the Forestry Commission will include the Forest Management Tables (out of print as Booklet 34) and will show the changes in yield associated with changes in initial spacing, line-thinning and delays in thinning (see p. 36).

Spacing

The initial crop spacings assumed for the discounted revenue (DR) tables are those that were current in the 1950s and early 60s because the available yield tables were set up for forecasting production from such stands. In the 1960s wider spacings of 1.7 m to 1.8 m came into vogue, subsequently extending as far as 2.1 m. These are economically more attractive in that they reduce establishment costs while not markedly affecting production other than decreasing the number of stems and increasing average stem diameter and volume at the time of first thinning. Despite these changes in practice, the tabulated DRs may also be employed for wider spaced crops in the knowledge that spacings of the order of 2 to 2.5 m will not markedly change the revenue values.

Stocking

Forestry Commission yield tables assume full stocking and the figures must be adjusted to allow for gaps resulting from crop failures of one form or another and for reduction in area resulting from roads, streams, buildings etc. This reduction factor varies with conditions, but 15 per cent has been assumed in the calculations of the DR tables here.

Felling and Thinning Regimes

The tables in Appendix 4 cover two possible management regimes: thinning in accordance with the Management Tables and no thinning. The timing of first thinnings (see Appendix 8) is the first age at which the stand can be thinned such that the volume increment will allow subsequent thinning on a 5 year cycle at the intensity stipulated in the Management Tables. The economically optimal age of first thinning may be somewhat later than this under certain circumstances and Part III sets out the type of calculation required to determine this age.

Wind

The effect of wind may be taken into account in a number of ways and is dealt with specifically in Part III, where questions of timing of thinning and clear felling are considered.

Prices

The prices used in the computations correspond to standing tree prices (i.e. marketing overheads are not included). These prices are based on average

8

values obtained by the Forestry Commission over the decade 1967 – 77 converted into £s of 76/77 value (average for April 1976 to March 1977). This price-size relationship which is shown graphically in Figure 1 and as a schedule in Appendix 2 is used in the revenue calculations which follow on the assumption that in the longer term average price levels for wood will not be different in *real* terms from those obtained over the decade 1967 – 77.

For analyses involving revenues to be obtained from early thinning or in the near future it may well be more realistic to use current local prices and allowance is made for this in Part III. Discounted volumes (DV) are equivalent to discounted revenues with the price per cubic metre taken as unity. If it is felt that the general price assumptions are, say, too low by £2 per cu m *over all sizes* then the tabulated DRs can be adjusted to take account of this by multiplying the appropriate DV (see Appendix 5) by £2 and adding this product to the original DR. If, on the other hand, it is felt that prices should be say 30 per cent higher than shown in Appendix 2 then an amended DR can be calculated by multiplying the tabulated figure by 1.30.

Where it is felt that the shape of the price-size curve shown in Figure 1 is inappropriate then the appraiser can use his own price-size relationship to generate DRs using full DV tables. These tables show volumes of thinnings and of main crop before thinning and their respective discounted volumes at a number of discount rates. Each element of DV can be multiplied by the price for the particular tree size to yield a DR element which summed give DR_o to a given age. An example of a layout is shown in Figure 2. When DV tables are not available the DV can be calculated quite easily by multiplying the volume given in a yield model appropriate to age and treatment by the factor (Appendix 1) for the period of discounting.

As noted above the prices used in computing the tabulated DR values are in £(76/77). It is important when comparing costs with revenues or when callating NDRs that both costs and revenues are assessed in £s of the same value. This means either deflating current costs back to 1976/77 levels if using the DRs given or inflating revenues to current £s. Indices for making these adjustments are contained in Appendix 3 and an example of their use is given in Part III, p 19.

Costs

Overhead costs (local supervision, office expenses etc.) should be included in the appraisal if a full assessment of the financial implications of a course

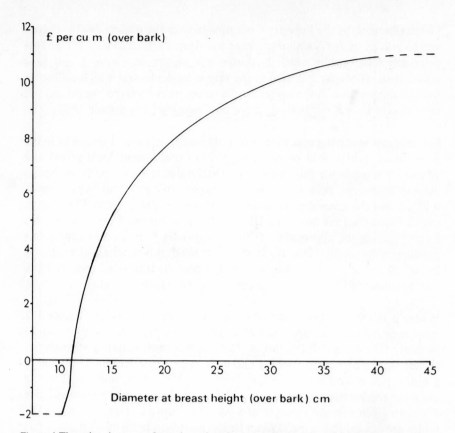

Figure 1 The price-size curve from data given in Appendix 2 and used in the example calculations. The negative values make allowance for harvesting costs being in excess of revenue.

of action is required. They should also be included if they are expected to differ between alternative projects. Otherwise it is suggested that the costs considered should be up to the level of wages, materials, machinery and labour overheads (sick pay, holidays, transport of workers etc.).

It is desirable to consider cost levels in recent years as well as the present in order to establish whether current costs are appropriate (for example, they may be abnormal as a result of unusual weather) and also whether there is any significant trend, either up or down. To do this it is necessary to inflate the unit costs of previous years into current £s using the factors given in Appendix 3.

Figure 2 An Example from Tables of Volumes Discounted to Year Zero derived from a Computer Printout

DISCOUNT RATES: 1.0 3.0 5.0 7.0 PERCENT

SCOTS PINE   YIELD CLASS 12   THINNING REGIME SP 1.4M 1.0MT   1 NEUTRAL + LOW   STOCKING PROP'N: .85

| (1) Age | THINNINGS | | | | | | FELLINGS | | | | | | (1) Age |
| | (2) Volume | (3) Mean tree | Discounted volumes at Year 0 | | | | (8) Volume | (9) Mean tree | Discounted volumes at Year 0 | | | | |
(years)	(cu.m)	(cu.m)	(4) 1%	(5) 3%	(6) 5%	(7) 7%	(cu.m)	(cu.m)	(10) 1%	(11) 3%	(12) 5%	(13) 7%	(years)
18	.0	.000	.0	.0	.0	.0	63.3	.018	52.9	37.2	26.3	18.7	18
23	37.8	.038	30.1	19.2	12.3	8.0	113.0	.038	89.9	57.3	36.8	23.8	23
29	35.7	.052	26.8	15.1	8.7	5.0	142.5	.072	106.8	60.5	34.6	20.0	29
34	35.7	.100	25.5	13.1	6.8	3.6	174.1	.135	124.1	63.7	33.1	17.4	34
39	35.7	.171	24.2	11.3	5.3	2.6	208.8	.225	141.7	65.9	31.1	14.9	39
44	35.7	.262	23.0	9.7	4.2	1.8	244.4	.340	157.7	66.6	28.6	12.5	44
49	35.7	.375	21.9	8.4	3.3	1.3	278.5	.478	171.0	65.4	25.5	10.1	49
54	35.7	.512	20.9	7.2	2.6	.9	309.4	.635	180.8	62.7	22.2	8.0	54
59	34.5	.637	19.2	6.0	1.9	.6	336.1	.806	186.9	58.8	18.9	6.2	59
64	31.6	.816	16.7	4.8	1.4	.4	359.1	.989	190.0	54.2	15.8	4.7	64
69	28.6	.971	14.4	3.7	1.0	.3	380.5	1.174	191.5	49.5	13.1	3.6	69
74	25.8	1.122	12.3	2.9	.7	.2	400.7	1.360	191.9	45.0	10.8	2.7	74
79	22.9	1.263	10.4	2.2	.5	.1	419.6	1.545	191.2	40.6	8.9	2.0	79
84	20.2	1.400	8.8	1.7	.3	.1	436.8	1.723	189.4	36.5	7.3	1.5	84
89	17.6	1.533	7.3	1.3	.2	.0	450.8	1.886	185.9	32.5	5.9	1.1	89
94	15.0	1.670	5.9	.9	.2	.0	461.1	2.027	181.0	28.6	4.7	.8	94
99	12.9	1.831	4.8	.7	.1	.0	471.2	2.156	176.0	25.3	3.8	.6	99

Effect of Taxation and Grants on Costs and Returns

Although these calculations show costs, revenues and net revenues as if they were exclusive of taxes, tax allowances and grants, it will usually be the case that a private individual or company is most interested in the cash flows, and their present value, after taxes and grants have been taken into account. Indeed, the only sensible method of appraisal of investments affected by taxation and grants is to compare costs net of tax allowances and grants with revenues after tax.

The main problem in estimating the position after tax and after grant concerns the identification of the investor and the beneficiary of the investment under appraisal. In most cases of plantation investment, the same individual will not receive the revenues flowing from the original outlay. This question of the treatment of future returns can be handled in one of two ways. The first is to consider the period of occupation of the woodland by one person. This creates its own problem, however, because a value has to be attached to a given stand before its planned life is complete. The second is to create the fiction of a continuing owner or occupier whose tax position may, if necessary, be supposed to alter favourably as a result of changes in ownership or occupation of a particular woodland. Although the case is hypothetical, it appears to be the most direct way of approaching the problem of appraisal for investments covering the bulk, or whole, of a crop's life.

Thus, for woodlands assessed under Schedule D, the required adjustment of costs to be incurred in the near future will not be difficult to calculate. If the marginal income tax rate applicable expressed as a fraction is t, the cost of allowable expenditure, assuming this does not exceed the amount in the tax band covered by t, is cost, net of any grants, times $(1 - t)$. For costs which are likely to be incurred some time into the future, such as pole-stage fertilisation or the cutting of inspection racks, a judgement must be made about whether these are likely to be relieved through Schedule D income tax or not because the woodland concerned may then be assumed to be taxed under Schedule B. In relation to revenues from thinnings and felling, the simplifying assumption of Schedule B income tax may be made.

In the case of capital taxation, it is suggested that for working purposes a judgement must be made on the effective rate of tax arising which, applied to revenues from the class of stand under consideration, is equivalent to the expected Capital Transfer Tax liability arising from a transfer at death.

III. Applications

The following examples cover the main sorts of appraisal that may be carried out during the life of a tree crop starting with land acquisition and finishing with the timing of clear felling. These examples follow the principles outlined in Part I and include assumptions detailed in Part II. If the particular decision area the reader is interested in is not covered in these examples it is hoped that sufficient guidance is given to enable him to undertake the appraisal from first principles.

Land Purchase

The value of a parcel of land for forestry depends on the cost of establishing and maintaining the tree crop and the value of the receipts expected from the produce. Total revenues minus total costs discounted back to the time of purchasing the land, which may be a year or two before the time of planting, represents the *expectation value* of the crop at whatever discount rate is deemed appropriate by the prospective purchaser. Assuming this expectation value, or net present value, is positive then this is the sum which the purchaser can afford to pay for the land and make a profit in real terms equal to the rate of discount used. If the expectation value is lower than the market price or worse still is negative (DE is greater than DR) then the land is only worth purchasing if:

i. the prospective owner expects additional non-market benefits (e.g. amenity and recreation) not included in the appraisal—tax benefits, grants and net revenues from sporting should have been included in the appraisal; or

ii. the purchaser expects the value of the land to increase in real terms (although this can be included explicitly in the appraisal).

The question of choice of species and management regime will be discussed in subsequent sections. The *Forest site yield guide to Upland Britain*

(Busby, 1974) may be of some help in this context. In the example below, the following assumptions are made:

species to be planted: Sitka spruce   50% of area $\left.\rule{0pt}{16pt}\right\}$ both crops to
                               Japanese larch   50% of area   be thinned.
expected yield class :   SS YC 12
                              JL YC 10
rate of discount   :   5%

The costs per hectare are set out below and their discounted value at the chosen discount rate of 5% shown in the right hand column.

	£(78/79)[a]	Year	Discounting factor	Discounted value
				£
preplanting road	10	− 1	1.05	10.5[e]
fencing	20	0	1.0	20.0
ploughing	40	0	1.0	40.0
planting	40	0	1.0	40.0
beating up	15	1	0.952	14.3
weeding	25	2	0.907	22.7
fertilising	35	10	0.614	21.5
roading[b]	50	16[c]	0.458	22.9
protection and maintenance	4.5 p/a	1 − 50[d]	18.26	82.2
				274.1

Notes
(a) These costs exclude overheads.
(b) Including upgrading of preplanting road.
(c) JL to be first thinned at 17 years.
(d) Felling age of maximum DR at 5% from Appendix 7:
SS = 55 years $\left.\rule{0pt}{14pt}\right\}$ (average = 50 years)
JL = 45 years
(e) Costs compounded forward one year to time of planting.

Revenues per Hectare

Using the tables in Appendix 4, which give values in £(76/77), we find the discounted revenue at 50 years for SS YC 12 (thinned) to be £385 per ha and for JL YC 10 (thinned) £390, which as the species are to be planted in equal proportions gives an average of £387.5.

14

Using the inflation factors from Appendix 3 it is evident that the net discounted revenue (NDR) of the crop in £(78/79) is (£387.5 × 1.2363) − £274.1 = £205.0, but this does not take into account:

i. the value of a successor crop, if the area is to continue in forestry;

ii. the value of the land at the end of the rotation for other purposes;

iii. the value of any other fixed assets such as roads and buildings left after the felling.

Assumptions about the value of successor crops or fixed assets 50 years hence can be no more than conjecture. However such matters do affect the calculation of the land value and there are two ways of dealing with this. The first is to assume that the area will be planted with the same species and hence produce a similar NDR, only differing because subsequent expenditure on roads is unlikely to be the same as in the life of the first crop. The other, equivalent, way is to ascribe a value to the land at the end of the first crop's life equal to that at the beginning. There may of course be other fixed assets remaining after the first crop has been cleared. It is assumed that roads are the only assets other than the land and that these are conservatively valued at one half their original cost, that is ½(50) or £25 per ha. The expectation value of the land, LV, is then calculated thus:

$$LV = 205 + (25 \times 0.087) + (LV \times 0.087)$$ Note: 0.087 is the discount factor for 50 years at 5%.

Crop   Discounted   Discounted
NDR   Residual   Residual
        Road Value   Land Value

$$LV(1 - 0.087) = 205 + 2.2 = 207.2$$

$$\text{Therefore } LV = \frac{207.2}{1 - 0.087}$$
$$= £227 \text{ per ha}$$

Any expected increase in land values in real terms would be included by adjusting the land value on the right hand side of the equation.

The sum of £227 represents the expectation value of the land per hectare at the time of planting. If there is to be a lapse of a year or two between purchase and planting this figure must be further discounted to account for that period. If the investor buys the land at this price, then on the stated assumptions the investment will make 5% in real terms.

It should be noted that LV depends on the felling age adopted. The land value determined in this calculation is close to the maximum since the felling ages assumed for the component crops are those which are likely to give the maximum DR at the chosen discount rate.

The investor may wish to do this calculation using the actual expected market price of land in order to determine the internal rate of return he might expect if he decides to go ahead with the investment. To do this he has to put the land value on the right hand side of the above equations and thereby determine the net present value (NPV) of the whole investment. The initial equation now becomes:

$$\begin{array}{cccccc} NPV = & Crop & + Discounted & + Discounted & - Cost \\ & NDR & Residual & Residual & of \\ & & Road\ Value & Land\ Value & Land \end{array}$$

If the expected market price of the land is £300 per ha and acquisition expenses are assumed to be £10 per ha, then the net present value at 5% in the above example is:

$$\begin{aligned} NPV &= 205 + (25 \times 0.087) + (300 \times 0.087) - 310 \\ &= -76.7 \end{aligned}$$

Repeating this calculation at 3% and at 7% and plotting the results would show that with the price of the land at £300 the net present value would be zero at 4½% and this is therefore the internal rate of return for the investment.

Choice of species

Site factors such as soil, vegetation and climate affect the choice of which species to plant. As the site factors become more adverse to tree growth so the choice of species becomes restricted. It is, of course, possible to ameliorate the adverse characteristics of the soil and ground vegetation by ploughing, draining and use of fertilisers.

On some sites the decision boils down to a choice between a high yielding species such as Sitka spruce requiring a fairly intensive establishment regime and a lower yielding but less exacting species such as Lodgepole pine which can be established and maintained at considerably less expense. Elsewhere, as on the more fertile sites, there may be a choice between larch with its short establishment period and early yields and, say, Douglas fir costing much more to establish but promising a much higher yield of timber.

The appraisal then reduces to the comparison of the alternative levels of expenditure and consequential returns. Take, for example, the Sitka/ Lodgepole choice on an unflushed peat at an elevation of 300 m in the Scottish Borders. Table 1 shows the fertiliser/herbicide regimes expected to be required to grow Sitka Yield Class 11 (SS YC 11) or Lodgepole Yield Class 8 (LP YC 8). The initial formation (application of a PK fertiliser, ploughing, draining and planting) is expected to be the same for both species and can therefore be ignored as can the cost of roading which, in practice, is unlikely to be significantly different either in density or timing for these two options. This leaves the comparison between the additional cost of the more intensive Sitka spruce fertiliser/herbicide regime and the gain in DR for SS YC 11 as against LP YC 8. The calculation is shown in Table 2.

Table 1 Expenditure on alternative herbicide and fertiliser regimes for SS and LP on unflushed peats

£ per ha

Operation		Sitka spruce					Lodgepole pine				
	Year	Expenditure	Discounted Expenditure			Year	Expenditure	Discounted Expenditure			
			3%	5%	7%			3%	5%	7%
Apply 2,4-D	5	25	21.6	19.6	17.8	–	–	–	–	–
PK	5	45	38.8	35.3	32.1	5	45	38.8	35.3	32.1
PK	10	45	33.5	27.6	22.9	–	–	–	–	–
P	–	–	–	–	–	15	25	16.0	12.0	9.1
N	15	40	25.7	19.2	14.5	–	–	–	–	–
NP	20	60	33.2	22.6	15.5	–	–	–	–	–
Totals		215	152.8	124.3	102.8		70	54.8	47.3	41.2

Note: initial applications of fertiliser before year 5 are the same for both species and have therefore been ignored.

Assuming both crops are to be thinned and will be felled at the age of maximum DR, the DR gain can be determined from Appendix 4 and compared with the additional DE, as shown in Table 2, ensuring that both expenditures and revenues are in £s of the same value. For example at 5% the gain in $DR_o = \frac{1}{2}(385 + 270) - 155 = £172.5$.

Table 2 Comparison of net gain/loss from choosing SS (YC 11) as against LP (YC 8)

	Discount Rate		
	3%	5%	7%
Additional DE_o (from Table 1)	98.0	77.0	61.6
Gain in DR_o (from Appendix 4)	402.5	172.5	77.5
Net gain/loss	+304.5	+95.5	+15.9

These results suggest that the choice of the high input regime with SS is more profitable than the low input LP at all three interest rates implying an internal rate of return of just over 7% at which point $DE = DR$. However, the long-term response to a fertiliser regime in forestry cannot be defined with any certainty and in such circumstances it is essential to undertake a sensitivity analysis to determine the effect of changes in assumption about the yields from the two regimes. For example, suppose the yield class of the SS is expected to lie between 10 and 12 and that for LP between 7 and 9. As the above analysis indicates that the SS high input regime is the more profitable, it is desirable to look at the sensitivity of the result to the lowest probable yield for SS (i.e. YC10) in comparison with the highest probable yield of LP (i.e. YC9). The DR_o gain, at say 5%, resulting from the use of SS instead of LP, becomes $270 - \frac{1}{2}(155 + 255) = £65$. This produces a net loss because the additional cost of the SS high input regime is £77 at 5% (see Table 2). This illustrates that in this appraisal the result is fairly sensitive to assumptions on yield class.

Fertilisation

Until further evidence is available on response to fertilisation in terms of volume and wood quality it is reasonable to make the assumption that the revenue gained by treatment can be found by reference to increase in top height over the life of the treated crop. Given an assessment of this total increase to rotation age, it is possible to assess the change in yield class over the life of the crop and hence the DR increase. For example the Management Tables show for Sitka spruce at a felling age of say 55 years, top heights of 20.2 m for YC 10 and 22.7 m for YC 12. Hence if an increase in top height of 2.5 m is expected as a result of treatment the gain in DR can be assessed by comparing the DR values for YC 12 and 10. The Booklet on fertilisers in the establishment of conifers in Wales and Southern England (Everard, 1974) gives guidance on the use of fertilisers.

Appraisal of Single Applications

Tables 3 and 4 apply only to unthinned stands, that is either pre-first thinning or non-thin regimes. For appraisal of crops already thinned it should be possible to measure the enhanced growth in terms of added volume, attribute a value to this and compare this value, suitably discounted to the time of the application of the fertiliser, with the cost of the applications. However, as the experimental evidence for the response to fertiliser application in pole stage and older crops is very limited, the following discussion is confined to the appraisal of the treatment of younger crops.

Table 3 Gain in DR_0 per 10 cm increase in top height at age of maximum DR

£(76/77) per ha

		Yield Class																	
		6			8			10			12			14			16		
		Discount Rate % 3	5	7	3	5	7	3	5	7	3	5	7	3	5	7	3	5	7
Crops to be	SS	7	3	1	9	4	2	11	5	2	13	6	3	14	7	4	15	8	5
thinned	LP	6	2	1	7	3	2	8	4	3	10	5	3	11	6	4			
Crop to be left *un-*	SS	6	3	1	7	3	2	8	4	2	9	4	3	10	5	3	11	6	4
thinned	LP	5	2	1	5	3	2	6	4	2	7	4	3	8	5	3			

Table 3 sets out the gain in DR at year U associated with a 10 cm increase in top height at the end of the crop's life. For example, suppose a single application of phosphate (P) applied to SS YC 10 at age 5 is expected to lead to an increase in top height over the succeeding say 10 years, and hence over the crop's life, of 75 cm. Then the gain in DR_0 at 5% for a thinned crop is £5 × 75/10 = £(76/77) 37.5 per ha. This figure £37.5 has to be compounded 5 years and inflated into £s of the same value as the expenditure. The DR compounded 5 years by a factor of 1.276 (from Appendix 1) and adjusted for inflation from 76/77 to 78/79 by a factor of 1.2363 (from

19

Appendix 3) yields a result of $37.5 \times 1.276 \times 1.2363 = £(78/79)59$. This compared with a cost of treatment of say £(78/79) 30 indicates that if the increase in height is achieved the investment will be profitable at 5%.

Allowance for Advancement in Age of First Thinning or of Felling

Increases in growth will affect the time of certain expenditures, and hence DE. Thus in crops which are to be thinned, the age of first thinning and hence roading and brashing may well have to be brought forward. In non-thin crops the felling age may be brought forward and hence roading costs may be incurred earlier.

For thinned crops the effect on DE will be limited to the influence of responses achieved before the age of first thinning. Table 4 sets out the period by which first thinning age is brought forward as a result of fertiliser responses obtained by that time, or the age of felling is brought forward for non-thin crops. For example, in the case quoted above, suppose the combined cost of roading is £200 per ha and the planned age of first thinning is 30 years (that is 4 years delay from the age indicated in the Management Tables). Then the roads element of DE at say 5% to year 5

Table 4 Reduction in age of first thinning/felling per 10 cm increase in top height of Sitka spruce and Lodgepole pine

Years

Yield class		6	8	10	12	14	16
Crops to be thinned(a)		.3	.2	.2	.2	.2	.2
Crops to be left unthinned	(b) 3%	.5	.4	.4	.3	.3	.3
	5%	.4	.4	.3	.3	.2	.2
	7%	.4	.3	.3	.2	.2	.2

Notes: (a) Assessed by reference to responses achieved by time of first thinning. These figures are independent of discount rate because the Management Table age of first thinning is specific to the yield class and is determined mensurationally.

(b) Discount rate. These figures have been assessed by reference to responses over the whole life of the crop. The figures vary with discount rate because the age of clear cutting (non-thin crops) is defined in this paper as the age of maximum DR and is therefore a function of the rate of discount used.

(when the fertiliser is to be applied) amounts to £200 × 0.295 (discounting factor for 25 years) or £59. For a height response of 75 cm the advancement is roughly 2 years (7.5 × 0.2 from Table 4) that is from year 30 to year 28. The roads and brashing element of DE_5 is £200 × 0.326 (discounting factor for 23 years) or £65. Thus the increase in DE is $65 - 59 = £6$ which therefore reduces the gain in DR_5 from £(78/79) 59 to £(78/79) 53. This value still exceeds the cost of fertilising.

Where major increases in growth are obtained by fertilisation, there will be cases where it is profitable to thin a crop which would otherwise be left unthinned. The appraisal is broken down into two stages. The first is to decide whether, for the Yield Class expected over the crop's life as a result of fertilising, thinning or no thinning is optimal, taking into consideration the main factors of bringing forward roading costs and possible changed liability to wind damage. The section on thinning (page 28) gives guidance on this point. Once the optimum thinning regime has been decided it is then simply a matter of calculating the difference between DR net of discounted roading and comparing this difference with the discounted cost of fertilising.

Appraisal of Multiple Applications

The appraisal of multiple applications of fertilisers is carried out in basically the same way as for single applications. The total height gain for the set of treatments has to be predicted and expenditure on each treatment is discounted to a common point in time and summed. In practice it is desirable during the course of a crop's life to reassess the economics of additional treatments in the light of local experience.

Sensitivity Analysis

As with the appraisal on choice of species, the results of this calculation are likely to be sensitive to assumptions on the yield responses to fertiliser applications and therefore sensitivity analysis is desirable. For example, suppose there is a possibility of the cost of treatment rising to £35 per ha and that the increment in top height as a result of treatment might be only 50 cm over the crop's life. The DR gain at 5% then falls below the cost of application and the investment is no longer viable at this rate of interest.

Beating up, Weeding and Cleaning

Recent work on the pre-tax financial implications of different spacings indicates that in most circumstances planting at 2 to 2½ m is desirable. Possibly on upland sites suffering from severe exposure the maximum spacing necessary to ensure speedy establishment may be a little less than this (Low, 1974), but in general the planting of more than 2,500 trees per hectare rarely appears to be justified.

Financial appraisal of the timing of first thinning at a range of discount rates indicates an optimum age some 5 years later than indicated in the Management Tables, except where windthrow is a significant risk (see section on thinning pp 28–32). Both the economics of the timing of first thinning and of spacing suggest that there should not be too much concern over scattered losses in a young crop providing the stocking at first thinning age is of the order of 1,500 stems per hectare (excluding roads and rides, etc.).

Where the losses are grouped such that there will be a gap in the canopy that will endure for a large part of the life of the crop, then an appraisal of whether to beat up (or weed or clean to prevent such losses) is desirable. The loss in discounted revenue can readily be calculated from the tables in Appendix 4. In the example below the question of whether to beat up or not is considered. The appraisal of weeding or cleaning and indeed, protection, follows the same basic principles.

Assume a crop of Sitka spruce YC14 is to be appraised 2 years after planting to determine the loss in DR as a result of large gaps in the crop estimated to cover 30 per cent of the area planted. The DR_o, at say 5%, expected for a thinned crop is £510 per hectare. Because the edge trees around the gap will grow more vigorously than if they had been within the stand the loss in DR will not be as high as 30 per cent. As a rough rule of thumb, a figure of two-thirds the initial percentage is probably a satisfactory guide. Thus in this example 20 per cent of the DR_o value is £102 and this represents the loss per planted hectare at year 0. It might be thought that this figure should be compounded forward, in this example to year 2, but this would only be appropriate if the beaten up plants were to grow faster than the initial planting and so make up for lost time (by not compounding forward some allowance is being made for the likely actual growth). In the case of weeding or cleaning, the DR_o should be compounded forward to the year of operation concerned.

In order to compare the estimated DR loss with the current cost of beating up (or weeding or cleaning) the former has to be brought into £s of the same year using the appropriate factor from Appendix 3. When estimating the costs involved it must not be forgotten that beating up may lengthen the period of establishment and additional weeding costs, suitably discounted, may also have to be allowed for.

Protection

In most examples of investment appraisal presented so far the physical consequences of a given course of action are more or less readily predictable, the volume yields, tree sizes and other features being assessed from sample plots and experiments. In the case of protection from animals, insects, fungi and man, the degree of damage by a particular agent is liable to be peculiar to the locality and crop and to be sporadic. Estimation of the probable damage for a given crop, degree of protection and external circumstances is the major difficulty in appraisal. A great deal depends, therefore, on the experience of the local manager, and the role of judgement in deciding the most favoured level of protection is far greater than in many other fields of applied forest economics.

The aim of maximising NDR means that it is worth spending up to the point when an extra £1 of expenditure produces only £1's worth of benefit. In the case of protection, the benefit is the reduction in losses. The rate of reduction in the value of losses just equals the rate of increase in expenditure at a point when the sum of the losses plus the expenditure is at a minimum. This concept of minimising the sum of costs plus losses is the basis for the first example below. The examples illustrate appraisal techniques where the value of loss is confined to reduction in wood revenue. There will, however, be cases in which values over and above wood production are considered important, in which case these should be incorporated in the appraisal.

One of the simplest ways of arriving at an approximate optimum level of expenditure is to consider a number of options (for example, a complete deer fence, or a full-time stalker, or regular shoots) and to estimate the probable level of damage associated with each option. This is easier said than done, but experience should enable plausible estimates to be made of the range of damage that might be expected to result from a particular course of action.

These levels of damage must be converted into loss in DR. This can be done with some precision by, for example, determining the likely number of trees which will be damaged and converting this into terms of loss of thinning yield and thence to revenue and DR. An easier and probably just as accurate method is to assess the damage in terms of delay in establishment and/or as the percentage of the crop lost over the life of the stand and to convert these into a reduction in DR by reference to the figures in Appendix 4. Having established the costs and losses associated with various options, which should always include the possibility of doing nothing, it is then only necessary to determine which option minimises the sum of the costs plus losses.

Suppose, for example, that within a 500 hectare block of conifers that has just moved into the thinning stage, 50 hectares of mature Sitka spruce have been clear felled and this area is to be replanted with SS with an expected yield class of 12. The ring fence round the whole block is in reasonable condition but there are a few breaks and deer are known to be in the block but not doing any damage to the pole stage crop. However, it is expected that they would almost certainly damage any restocking. Four options might be considered:

A. No action—only 80 per cent of area established and then only after a delay of 10 years;

B. Employ contract stalker when deer causing damage, at a cost of £500 per annum (net of any income from sale of venison etc.) and leave ½ hectare unplanted as a deer lawn—only 49½ hectare planted, 10 per cent of which fails to become established;

C. Deer fence 50 hectare block at cost of £5,000 plus £50 per annum for maintenance for 10 years—5 per cent of area lost;

D. Repair and maintain existing fence around 500 hectare block at an initial cost of £500 plus £200 per annum maintenance for the next 10 years (in practice the fence would be repaired intermittently) and employ part-time stalker for 4 months a year at a total cost (net of any income) of £1,300 per annum—full crop established.

From Appendix 4, DR_o values for SS YC12 are £1,005, 385 and 170 at 3, 5 and 7% respectively. The costs plus losses of the four options are set out in Table 5.

Table 5 Comparison of four wildlife protection options

£

Option	A	B	C	D
Costs				
Year 0	—	—	5000	500
1–10	—	500	50	1500
DE_o at 3%	—	4265	5427	13295
5%	—	3861	5386	12083
7%	—	3512	5351	11035
Losses	20% DR plus 10 years delay	10% DR plus ½ha unplanted	5% DR	—
DR_o at 3%	$50 \times 1005 \times$ $[1 - (0.8 \times 0.774)]$ $= 19135$	$49½ (1005 \times 0.1)$ $= 5477$	$50 (1005 \times 0.05)$ $= 2513$	—
5%	$50 \times 385 \times$ $[1 - (0.8 \times 0.614)]$ $= 9794$	$49½ (385 \times 0.1)$ $= 2098$	$50 (385 \times 0.05)$ $= 962$	—
7%	$50 \times 170 \times$ $[1 - (0.8 \times 0.508)]$ $= 5046$	$49½ (170 \times 0.1)$ $= 927$	$50 (170 \times 0.05)$ $= 425$	—
Costs plus losses				
NPV_o at 3%	19135	9742	**7940**	13295
5%	9794	**5959**	6348	12083
7%	6975	**4439**	5776	11035

Note: Figures in bold type indicate the least (cost + loss) at each test discount rate.

As might be expected the choice of option varies to some extent with the discount rate; it will of course be desirable to test the sensitivity of the choice to both the cost and loss assumptions.

The same concept of minimising costs plus losses applies equally to fire protection, but there is then the added complication that if the area burnt is sufficiently large it may warrant immediate replanting. It may even reopen the question of desirable land use, but in most circumstances a change in land use as a result of fire is unlikely. Assuming that the area burnt will be replanted then the cost of damage can be calculated as:

The revenue loss through postponement of yield as a result of having to replant, plus the initial restocking cost, less costs of operations no longer required (for example, fencing) less postponement of expenditures not now required until later as a result of having to replant (for example, roading) less value of salvage.

In symbols, the value of loss equals

$$p\ [DR_o\ (k^n - 1) + DE_{o\text{-}n} - X - DE_{n\text{-}f}\ (1 - k^{-n}) - S]$$

DR foregone n years		Restocking costs less operations no longer required		Postponement of later expenditures n years		Value of any salvage
	+		—		—	

where
p = probability of the plantation being burnt at year n
n = average age of plantation likely to burn
f = felling age
$DE_{o\text{-}n}$ = initial expenditure until time that plantation is burnt
X = discounted cost to year 0 of operations no longer required in the establishment of a new crop
$DE_{n\text{-}f}$ = expenditure that would have been incurred from age n to time of felling
k = compounding factor for n years to bring DR_o to DR_n
S = salvage value of burnt crop (if any)

Multiplying the value of loss at any given age by the probability of loss gives expected average loss. The cost of operations such as fire patrols, road building and provision of water tanks has then to be assessed together with the associated probabilities of damage. Thus the relationship might be as shown in Table 6.

Table 6 Comparison of five fire protection options

Option	A	B	C	D	E
(a) protection expenditure £/hectare/per annum	0	0.25	0.50	0.75	1.00
(b) probability of losing plantation by fire in an average year	.010	.002	.001	.0007	.0005
(c) value of loss, say £500 per hectare times probability (b)	5.00	1.00	0.50	0.35	0.25
(d) Total cost plus loss (a + c)	5.00	1.25	**1.00**	1.10	1.25

These results suggest that, in this example, expenditure in the region of 50p a year per hectare results in minimising costs plus losses. However, this is only an illustration and the figures should not be given any more credence than that. The major problem is the derivation of the probabilities related to the different levels of expenditure. Only experience can help here and even then it is specific to the vegetation and locality (the hazard and risk) of the area in question.

Roading

The subjects of road standard and road spacing are discussed in Rowan (1976) with illustrations of the method of appraising different lengths and types of road in a given block. The calculations on harvesting roads refer to roading just before the start of thinning but there is no reason why the appraisal should not relate to different times of road construction such as the time of establishment. It is assumed that the aim is to minimise the sum of road construction and discounted maintenance costs plus the discounted costs of loading, moving and unloading the trees harvested over the crop's life. In order to simplify the calculation, an average cost of extraction per cubic metre is nominated for the removal of all thinnings and the final felling. Then instead of calculating the relevant extraction costs for each and every cut, discounting these to the time of roading and summing them, the short-cut procedure is adopted of multiplying the nominated extraction cost by discounted volume (DV). The tables in Appendix 5 show discounted volume for thinned stands (after a 15 per cent reduction for gaps, roads etc.) calculated at 3, 5 and 7% to year 0. For any later year of roading up to the age of first thinning, the figures should be compounded using the factors in Appendix 1. If roading is delayed until after first thinning, the discounted volume is influenced by the amount of thinning already carried out, and for working purposes the discounted volume from remaining thinnings and final crop can be estimated sufficiently accurately by interpolation between the DV calculated to the year of first thinning and the final crop yield. Thus for Sitka spruce YC14, first thinning and roading are planned in, say, year 22, DV_0 at 5% = 77 (from Appendix 5) which compounded forward 22 years equals 225. The final crop yield at age 50 from the Management Tables, is 371 (main crop) plus 45 (thinnings) or 416 cu m per ha; and after adjustment for 15 per cent gaps, equals 354 cu m per ha. If roading is being appraised at age 35, 13 years after the Management Table age of first thinning, the discounted volume equals $225 + 13/28 \times (354 - 225) = 285$ cu m per ha. The fraction 13/28 represents the period from the Management Table age of first thinning to the time of roading (assuming thinning has gone on in the interim period) divided by the interval between first thinning and clearfelling.

Most woodlands contain a range of yield classes and ages and there is usually more than one species. An adequate measure of discounted volume can be found by averaging yield class (a worked example is provided by Rowan) and planting year and then referring to the discounted volume table for the dominant species and compounding up for the average age of the block.

Thinning

Thinning practice has long been the subject of fierce debate and will no doubt continue to be so. If crops are to be thinned, and that may well be the issue to be resolved, there are choices to be made on the age of first thinning, the intensity of thinning, the thinning cycle, the type of thinning (selective, namely crown or low, or systematic) and the age at which thinning should cease. The answers to each of these will depend on such factors as the owner's objectives, the markets available at the time and likely to be available in the future, the quality of the stand, its liability to wind damage and the implication of the terrain for harvesting methods and hence cost. This account is not intended as a treatise on these and other aspects of thinning that may concern the woodland owner but instead is intended to serve as a guide to the major issue of whether to thin and, if so, when. The Forestry Commission's Management Tables* (1971, Part II) discusses thinning policy in terms of intensity, cycle (and hence weight) and type. The intensity of thinning, or annual amount removed per hectare, is set in the Tables at 70 per cent of the yield class. This rate has been calculated to be on the slightly conservative side of the optimum if the aim is to maximise NDR at discount rates of between 3 and 5%. A higher intensity may be favoured if the owner is impatient to gain more revenue in the near future, but such cutting runs the risk of reducing the growing stock to a point at which less than full volume increment is produced. The following discussion therefore assumes the Management Table intensity and concentrates on the issue of time of thinning.

---

*These Tables will be reproduced by the Forestry Commission during 1981 in a new format— *Yield Models for Forest Management.*

Inspection of the figures for DR_o in Appendix 4 shows that at lower yield classes in all the main conifer species, the discounted revenue expected from a stand first thinned at the age noted in the Management Tables is less than that of an unthinned crop, allowance for mortality having been made in the yield tables on which these DR results are based. This is because small early thinnings are assumed to be unprofitable (see price-size schedule in Appendix 2). The tables of Appendix 4 are intended as a guide for comparisons between species, taking account of broad differences between discounted revenues from thinning and no-thinning, at the time of planting. They do not however provide guidance on the optimum timing of thinning. Recently produced yield models for the main conifer species covering line thinning of crops with thinning at Management Tables time (MTT), 5 years later than these ages (MT plus 5) and 10 years later (MT plus 10) show that with the price-size curve of Figure 1 higher values of DR can often be obtained with some delay in the start of thinning.

This effect would be offset if higher prices (of the order of £2 to 5 per cu m depending on yield class) were obtained for trees of around 0.04 cu m (Figure 1 assumes a net loss of £1 per cu m for trees of this size). Conversely lower prices for small trees make a later start to thinning relatively more profitable assuming that the risk of windthrow is not such as to make a delay in first thinning unacceptable. Further, where crops are unroaded, delay in installing roads is attractive and when the costs of roading are taken into account the maximum DR net of road costs and, where applicable, brashing costs, arises at later ages than apply in crops which are already roaded. Because of the variety of thinning regimes that can be applied, differences in the price of thinnings of various sizes from place to place, and differences in the costs of access and risk of windthrow, it is difficult to make general rules about the course of management which is likely to produce maximum net discounted revenue. However, given some assumptions about these factors and with the aid of some generalised tables, it is possible to calculate the most profitable course of action.

Figure 3 shows the general relationship of thinning regimes to yield class and to windthrow hazard (Booth, 1977) whilst Appendix 6 sets out values of discounted revenue for Sitka spruce calculated to the age of first thinning of the Management Tables for the three discount rates 3, 5 and 7% assuming the price-size curve of Figure 1. The time to which values are discounted has no relative effect on the results as long as it is the same for all the regimes being compared. However, as appraisal will normally be carried out towards the Management Table time (MTT) of first thinning (see Appendix 8), it is sensible to use this as the point to which values are discounted.

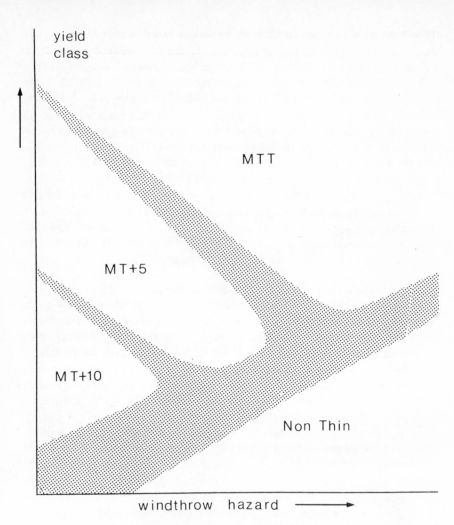

Figure 3 Relationship of thinning regime to yield class and windthrow hazard

MTT = Management Table time of first thinning
MT + 5 = Delay first thinning 5 years
MT + 10 = Delay first thinning 10 years.

The example in Table 7 calculates the optimum time for first thinning at a discount rate of 5% for an unroaded area of SS YC 12 in which the total cost of roading is £150 per hectare and road maintenance is expected to amount to £1.5 per hectare per year thereafter.

Table 7 Determination of optimum time of first thinning for Sitka spruce YC 12

		Management regime option			
		MTT	MT + 5 yrs	MT + 10 yrs	Non-thin
SITKA SPRUCE YC 12	Age at first thinning	24	29	34	—
	Age at felling	55	55	55	45
Discount rate 5%	Time of roading	24	29	34	45
	Years of road maintenance	31	26	21	—
A. Discounted revenue to Management Table age of first thinning (24 years) from Appendix 6		(a) 1230	1295	1280	(a) 1090
B. Calculation of discounted expenditure[b] per ha (to MT age of first thinning)					
1. Capital road cost per ha		150	150	150	150
2. Capitalised road maintenance annual cost of £1.5 per ha from time of first thinning to time of clear felling		23	22	19	0
3. Delay (X years) of roading compared with MT age of first thinning		0	5	10	21
4. Discount factor for X years		1	0.784	0.614	0.359
5. Total capitalised road cost discounted to MT age of first thin [(1 + 2) × 4] = variable DE		173	135	104	54
C. NDR = (A − B5)		1057	1160	1176	1036

Note: (a) These figures differ slightly from the Appendix 4 DR_0 values compounded forward 24 years, because the results in Appendix 6 have been smoothed across yield classes.

         (b) Brashing costs are assumed to be zero since the DRs are derived from yield models which assume the first thinning is a line thinning.

In the example, maximum NDR occurs with thinning starting 5 to 10 years later (MT + 5 to 10) than the age of 24 implied by the Management Tables.

Appraisal of the decision on timing of thinning is often complicated by the presence in a block of a number of different species, ages of plantation and yield classes. In most cases it is adequate to adopt a single calculation based on a weighted average assumption for age of first thinning, yield class and hence DR, using area of each crop as the weight.

The values in row A of the calculation will be significantly different where the hazard of windthrow is high. Objective knowledge of how windthrow risk changes with the age of a stand and with different heights and kinds of first thinning is at present almost entirely restricted to Sitka spruce. For this species, estimates have been made of the height at which windthrow may on average be expected to start in a crop of a given Windthrow Hazard Class (Booth 1977). In addition, assessments of the rate of progress of wind damage with different treatments has been made which allow the 'terminal height' to be estimated. This is the height at which it is judged such significant damage has occurred that felling of the crop is justified. A loss of about one-third of the growing stock appears to be a reasonable measure of this point. Table 8 sets out some broad estimates of terminal heights for Sitka spruce.

Table 8 Provisional estimates of terminal heights for MT age of thinning and for non-thin: Sitka spruce

Windthrow Hazard Class	III	IV	V	VI
Onset height, metres	19	16	13	10
Terminal height, metres: MT Age of First Thinning	24	20	16	12
Terminal height, metres: Non-thin	27	23	19	15

Given assumptions on terminal height it is a simple matter to find the ages implied in different yield classes and to calculate the expected discounted revenues to these ages. Using the lay-out of Table 8, it is then possible to make an objective decision, for Sitka spruce at least, about the best thinning practice in areas subject to windthrow. It must be added however that these figures are based on limited evidence from silvicultural experiments and should be regarded as only indicative.

The type of first thinning (selective or systematic) has an effect on DR apart from changed liability to wind damage (Hamilton, 1980). When allowance is made for the reduced harvesting costs in line-thinned crops and the lower cost of access through inspection racks as opposed to brashing, available information on yields indicates that where the risk of windthrow is negligible or slight, line thinning is more profitable in Sitka spruce, Norway spruce and Douglas fir, that line thinning or low thinning are about equally profitable in Scots pine and Corsican pine and that low thinning is favoured in Lodgepole pine and Japanese larch. Where there is risk of windthrow the desirable treatment is less clear cut and no general guidance is possible at present.

Timing of Felling and Crop Replacement

The optimum felling age is defined here as the age when the net discounted revenue from the existing and successor crops combined is maximised. The implication of fixing felling age by reference to maximum NDR at a given discount rate is that the current rate of return on capital, represented by growing stock and land, equals the chosen interest rate at that age.

The curve of NDR against felling age is fairly flat near the point of culmination and therefore the value of NDR is insensitive to changes in felling age within a range of plus or minus 5 years or so. Local marketing opportunities should influence the actual timing of the felling, higher than normal prices advancing the timing and a short-term market recession delaying it. Other considerations such as taxation, sporting and landscaping may well have an overriding effect on the timing of clear felling.

Where the successor crop NDR (including allowance for land value) is 0, that is the successor crop makes a return just equal to the discount rate, then the felling ages are as shown in Appendix 7. When the successor crop is expected to make a large positive NDR then some degree of advancement of felling age is justified on economic grounds.

The general rule is that a positive successor crop of NDR of up to £200 per ha will not advance the economic optimum felling age shown in Appendix 7 by more than 5 years and it is not until the successor crop NDR is more than £500 per ha that the felling age of the existing crop is advanced by between 5 and 10 years. The actual values vary with species, yield class and discount rate and can be specifically determined using the data in Appendix 4.

A sufficiently close estimate of the successor crop NDR can be found by deducting from the DR value shown in Appendix 4 the sum of the undiscounted formation costs. Fixed costs, such as protection and forest and road maintenance expenditure which apply whether the current crop is felled now or at some future date, can be ignored. There may be some post-establishment costs such as those of cleaning and brashing. These have only a small effect on optimum replacement ages and can normally also be ignored. The formation costs used should be those locally applicable, including preparation of ground, redraining, planting, beating-up and weeding, inclusive of labour oncost. For example, if the successor crop is Corsican pine YC14 (thinned), reference to Appendix 4 shows that the DR at say 5% is £505 per ha. Assuming total formation costs are £250 per ha, the successor crop NDR is £255 per ha, implying that the existing crop should be felled some 5 years earlier than the age given in Appendix 7.

Frequently the clearfelling of one stand has to be linked with that of a neighbour, whether for reasons of extraction or to reduce windthrow risk. In such cases the NDR for the whole felling coupe should be calculated for a series of felling ages in order to obtain the optimum. However, a reasonable approximation may be calculated by taking a weighted average (using area) of the individual felling ages.

Replacement of Unsatisfactory Crops

It does not follow that because a crop is judged to be unsatisfactory on silvicultural grounds, for example, poorly stocked, unhealthy or of lower growth rate than an alternative species, it should be replaced at the earliest opportunity. Unless considerations of forest hygiene demand the early removal of a source of potential infection it will often be more profitable to keep an unsatisfactory crop on the ground than to clearfell and replace it at an early stage. Once past the establishment phase, quite poor crops will often be capable of growth in value which places them at an advantage compared with replacement crops requiring new investment before they can produce any greater contributions to revenue. This point applies equally to broadleaves (where these are not being retained for amenity reasons alone) or when considering whether to accept natural regeneration or to replace it by planting another species or provenance.

Further, of two stands which are growing at different rates, it will not necessarily be true that the slower growing one should be replaced first. It may well be that the faster growing crop occupies a better site on which an alternative species would be relatively much more profitable than the alternative species on the poorer site.

Premature Felling in Anticipation of Windthrow

In some parts of the country there is a high risk of crops being blown down before they reach the age of economic maturity. Because of the costs associated with windthrow it is often considered desirable to fell crops prematurely before they become too vulnerable. The problem is to determine how vulnerable a crop needs to be before it is worth considering premature felling given various assumptions on the cost of windthrow.

Allowing windthrow to happen rather than felling prematurely has two potential disadvantages:

i. the volume recovered after windthrow may be less than the amount expected if the crop had remained standing, either through snapping of the stems or through a loss of production pending clearance of the site;

ii. the surplus value per cubic metre may be reduced because of increased harvesting costs and, in the case of large windthrows, owing to depressed prices in markets, increased transport costs and the managerial costs of reorganising harvesting and marketing.

These effects can be expressed as a percentage reduction in volume harvested and as a penalty in pence per cubic metre, the latter being a combination of the reduction in timber value and increased harvesting costs.

On the other hand, premature felling can result in a considerable reduction in revenue, depending upon the age of the crop. It is not worth felling prematurely unless the cost of windthrow times the probability of windthrow actually happening exceeds the revenue foregone as a result of premature felling. It is therefore necessary to compare the revenue foregone from felling prematurely by a number of years, with the cost of windthrow. As windthrow is not a certainty this latter cost must be multiplied by the probability (which must lie between 0 and 100 per cent) of windthrow actually occurring during that period.

Appraisals have been undertaken on Sitka spruce, assuming reductions in volume harvested of up to 10 per cent and harvesting cost and timber value penalties of up to £1 per cubic metre, to assess the magnitude of the probability required to warrant premature felling. At a discount rate of 5%, the results show that premature felling 5 years earlier than the age shown in Appendix 7 requires a probability of windthrow of the order of 20 to 50 per cent during the next 5 years of the crop's life, depending on the loss of volume and increase in harvesting costs etc. expected as a result of windthrow. Premature felling by as much as 10 years requires a probability of windthrow in the next 5 years of more than 50 per cent. A 3% discount rate would increase the required probability and a 7% rate would reduce it. As the assessment of the probability of windthrow is highly subjective, precise calculations of predicted loss of volume, additional harvesting costs and reduction in timber values, and hence the probability required to advance felling age, are hardly justified, but some working rules such as those indicated may be useful.

References

Booth, J C (1977)   *Windthrow hazard classification*   Forestry Commission Research Information Note 22/77/SILN.

Busby, R J N (1974)   *Forest site yield guide to Upland Britain* Forestry Commission Forest Record 97, HMSO, London.

Edwards, P N and Christie, J M (1981)   *Yield models for forest management*   Forestry Commission Booklet 48, Forestry Commission, Edinburgh.

Everard, J E (1974)   *Fertilisers in the establishment of conifers in Wales and Southern England*   Forestry Commission Booklet 41, HMSO, London.

Hamilton, G J (1980)   *Line thinning*   Forestry Commission Leaflet 77, HMSO, London.

Hamilton, G J and Christie, J M (1971)   *Forest management tables (metric)*   Forestry Commission Booklet 34, HMSO, London.

Hamilton, G J and Christie, J M (1974)   *Influence of spacing on crop characteristics and yield*   Forestry Commission Bulletin 52, HMSO, London.

Low, A J (1974)   *Initial spacing in relation to establishment and early growth of conifer plantations*   Research and Development Paper 110, Forestry Commission.

Rowan, A A (1976)   *Forest road planning*   Forestry Commission Booklet 43, HMSO, London.

Further reading

Blatchford, O N (Editor) (1978)   *Forestry practice*   9th Edition, Forestry Commission Bulletin 14, HMSO, London.

Garforth, M F (1979)   Mixtures of Sitka spruce and Lodgepole pine in South Scotland: history and future management   *Scottish Forestry* **33**(1).

Hart, C E (1979)   *Private Woodlands: a guide to British timber prices and forestry costings*   Hart, Coleford.

Hamilton, G J (1976)   *Aspects of thinning,*   Forestry Commission Bulletin 55, HMSO, London.

Johnston, D R, Grayson, A J and Bradley R T (1967)   *Forest planning*   Faber, London.

McIntosh, R (1978)   Response of Sitka spruce to remedial fertilisation in Galloway   *Scottish Forestry* **32**(4).

Appendix 1

Compound Interest Tables at 3, 5 and 7 percent

In the following three tables, factors and multipliers given for 1 to 100 years have been determined by the equations quoted.

Column (1) *Single payment compounding factor* $= (1+r)^n$ to give future value of £1 *compounded* for n years at an interest rate of r%.

Column (2) *Single payment discounting factor* $= 1/(1+r)^n$ to give present value of £1 *discounted* over n years at an interest rate of r%.

Column (3) *Compounded annual payment multiplier* $= [(1+r)^n - 1]/r$ to give future value in n years of a series of annual payments of £1 from present time to year n at an interest rate of r%.

For example, with $r = 5\%$, the accumulated cost of a £1 annual maintenance charge incurred over 20 years is £33.1.

Column (4) *Discounted annual payment multiplier* $= [(1+r)^n - 1]/r(1+r)^n$ to give the present value of a series of annual payment from present time to year n at an interest rate of r%.

For example, with $r = 7\%$, the discounted cost of a £1 annual maintenance charge incurred over 20 years is £10.6.

3%

(a) Compound Interest Factors at 3%

| n | Single Payment | | Equal Annual Payment | |
	Compounding factor (1)	Discounting factor (2)	Compounded multiplier (3)	Discounted multiplier (4)
1	1.030	0.97087	1.000	0.97087
2	1.061	0.94260	2.030	1.91347
3	1.093	0.91514	3.091	2.82861
4	1.126	0.88849	4.184	3.71710
5	1.159	0.86261	5.039	4.57971
6	1.194	0.83748	6.468	5.41719
7	1.230	0.81309	7.662	6.23028
8	1.267	0.78941	8.892	7.01969

9	1.305	0.76642	10.159	7.78611
10	1.344	0.74409	11.464	8.53020
11	1.384	0.72242	12.808	9.25263
12	1.426	0.70138	14.192	9.95401
13	1.469	0.68095	15.618	10.63496
14	1.513	0.66112	17.086	11.29608
15	1.558	0.64186	18.599	11.93794
16	1.605	0.62317	20.157	12.56111
17	1.653	0.60502	21.762	13.16612
18	1.702	0.58739	23.414	13.75352
19	1.754	0.57029	25.117	14.32380
20	1.806	0.55368	26.870	14.87748
21	1.860	0.53755	28.677	15.41503
22	1.916	0.52189	30.537	15.93692
23	1.974	0.50669	32.453	16.44361
24	2.033	0.49193	34.426	16.93555
25	2.094	0.47761	36.459	17.41315
26	2.157	0.46369	38.553	17.87685
27	2.221	0.45019	40.710	18.32704
28	2.288	0.43708	42.931	18.76411
29	2.357	0.42435	45.219	19.18846
30	2.427	0.41199	47.575	19.60045
35	2.814	0.35538	60.462	21.48722
40	3.262	0.30656	75.401	23.11478
45	3.782	0.26444	92.720	24.51872
50	4.384	0.22811	112.797	25.72977
55	5.082	0.19677	136.072	26.77443
60	5.892	0.16973	163.054	27.67557
70	7.918	0.12630	230.594	29.12342
80	10.641	0.09398	321.363	30.20077
90	14.300	0.06993	443.349	31.00241
100	19.219	0.05203	607.288	31.59891

Appendix 1 (*continued*)

(b) Compound Interest Factors at 5%

n	Single Payment		Equal Annual Payment	
	Compounding factor (1)	Discounting factor (2)	Compounded multiplier (3)	Discounted multiplier (4)
1	1.050	0.95238	1.000	0.95238
2	1.103	0.90703	2.050	1.85941
3	1.158	0.86384	3.153	2.72325
4	1.216	0.82270	4.310	3.54595
5	1.276	0.78353	5.526	4.32948
6	1.340	0.74622	6.802	5.07569
7	1.407	0.71068	8.142	5.78637
8	1.477	0.67684	9.549	6.46321
9	1.551	0.64461	11.027	7.10782
10	1.629	0.61391	12.578	7.72174
11	1.710	0.58468	14.207	8.30641
12	1.796	0.55684	15.917	8.86325
13	1.886	0.53032	17.713	9.39357
14	1.980	0.50507	19.599	9.89864
15	2.079	0.48102	21.579	10.37966
16	2.183	0.45811	23.657	10.83777
17	2.292	0.43630	25.840	11.27407
18	2.407	0.41552	28.132	11.68959
19	2.527	0.39573	30.539	12.08532
20	2.653	0.37689	33.066	12.46221

21	2.786	0.35894	35.719	12.82115
22	2.925	0.34185	38.505	13.16300
23	3.072	0.32557	41.430	13.48857
24	3.225	0.31007	44.502	13.79864
25	3.386	0.29530	47.727	14.09394
26	3.556	0.28124	51.113	14.37519
27	3.733	0.26785	54.669	14.64303
28	3.920	0.25509	58.403	14.89813
29	4.116	0.24295	62.323	15.14107
30	4.322	0.23138	66.439	15.37245
35	5.516	0.18129	90.320	16.37419
40	7.040	0.14205	120.800	17.15909
45	8.985	0.11130	159.700	17.77407
50	11.467	0.08720	209.348	18.25593
55	14.636	0.06833	272.713	18.63347
60	18.679	0.05354	353.584	18.92929
70	30.426	0.03287	588.529	19.34268
80	49.561	0.02018	971.229	19.59646
90	80.730	0.01239	1594.608	19.75226
100	131.501	0.00760	2610.026	19.84791

Appendix 1 (*continued*)

(c) Compound Interest Factors at 7%

7%

n	Single Payment		Equal Annual Payment	
	Compounding factor (1)	Discounting factor (2)	Compounded multiplier (3)	Discounted multiplier (4)
1	1.070	0.93458	1.000	0.93458
2	1.145	0.87344	2.070	1.80802
3	1.225	0.81630	3.125	2.62432
4	1.311	0.76290	4.440	3.38721
5	1.403	0.71299	5.751	4.10020
6	1.501	0.66634	7.153	4.76654
7	1.606	0.62275	8.654	5.38929
8	1.718	0.58201	10.260	5.97130
9	1.838	0.54393	11.978	6.51523
10	1.967	0.50835	13.816	7.02358
11	2.105	0.47509	15.784	7.49867
12	2.252	0.44401	17.888	7.94269
13	2.410	0.41496	20.141	8.35765
14	2.579	0.38782	22.550	8.74547
15	2.759	0.36245	25.129	9.10791
16	2.952	0.33873	27.888	9.44665
17	3.159	0.31657	30.840	9.76322
18	3.380	0.29586	33.999	10.05909
19	3.617	0.27651	37.379	10.33559
20	3.870	0.25842	40.995	10.59401

21	4.141	0.24151	44.865	10.83553
22	4.430	0.22571	49.006	11.06124
23	4.741	0.21095	53.436	11.27219
24	5.072	0.19715	58.177	11.46933
25	5.427	0.18425	63.249	11.65358
26	5.807	0.17220	68.676	11.82578
27	6.214	0.16093	74.484	11.98671
28	6.649	0.15040	80.698	12.13711
29	7.114	0.14056	87.347	12.27767
30	7.612	0.13137	94.461	12.40904
35	10.677	0.09366	138.237	12.94767
40	14.974	0.06678	199.635	13.33171
45	21.002	0.04761	285.749	13.60552
50	29.457	0.03395	406.529	13.80075
55	41.315	0.02420	575.929	13.93994
60	57.946	0.01726	813.520	14.03918
70	113.989	0.00877	1614.134	14.16039
80	224.234	0.00446	3189.062	14.22201
90	441.103	0.00227	6287.185	14.25333
100	867.716	0.00115	12381.661	14.26925

Appendix 2

Price-size schedule for conifers
Standing trees values in £ (76/7) per cu m[a]

Mean dbh (cms)	Price	Mean Volume[b] (cu m ob)	
		SS	SP
11	− 1.00[c]	0.04	0.04
12	1.90	0.06	0.06
13	3.21	0.07	0.07
14	4.27	0.09	0.09
16	5.83	0.14	0.14
18	6.87	0.20	0.19
20	7.63	0.25	0.25
22	8.29	0.35	0.35
24	8.87	0.40	0.40
26	9.37	0.50	0.45
28	9.79	0.60	0.50
30	10.13	0.70	0.60
32	10.39	0.85	0.75
34	10.60	1.05	0.90
36	10.77	1.25	1.05

| 38 | | 10.90 | | 1.45 | | 1.20 |
| 40 and above | | 11.00 | | 1.70 | | 1.35 |

Notes: (a) Based on average values obtained by the Forestry Commission over the decade 1967–77 converted to £s of 76/7 value. These averages are an amalgam of prices obtained from standing sales and net standing returns for timber worked by Forestry Commission labour.

(b) These figures are approximate. SS and SP cover the range of volumes for a given mean diameter for most species. CP and GF are similar to SS whilst LP, JL, DF and NS lie roughly midway between SS and SP. WH lies somewhat above SS. A more precise relationship can be calculated from the *Forest Management Tables* (Hamilton and Christie, 1971) and from Forestry Commission *Yield Models for Forest Management* (Edwards and Christie, 1981).

(c) This value makes allowance for harvesting costs being in excess of revenue.

Appendix 3

Factors for adjusting for inflation
General index of prices [1] for the United Kingdom (1976/77[2] = 100)

Financial Year (April to March)	Index	Year on Year[3] Change %
71/72	49.70	+ 9.6
72/73	54.48	
73/74	58.76	+ 7.9
74/75	71.48	+21.6
75/76	88.80	+24.2
76/77	100.00	+12.6
77/78	111.60	+11.7
78/79	123.63	+10.7
79/80	140.82	+13.9
80/81[4]	165.00	+17.2

(1) GDP implicit price deflator derived from various issues of *Economic Trends* up to July, 1980.
(2) April 1976—March 1977.

(3) Full year on previous year, not, as in many calculations of price change, last month of year on same month of previous year.

(4) Estimated.

The use of a deflator which measures the changing value of the £, in other words the purchasing power of the £, is appropriate where the question asked is how have costs, prices, expenditures or revenues changed in real terms. No single index can do this perfectly because there is no single right answer to the problem. The country's national income statistics do however provide as good and general a source as one can find. There are several measures available but on grounds of ease of access the one preferred is the gross domestic product (GDP) *implicit price deflator*. Values of this index are given above. The national income statistics show GDP by years and by quarters at both current and constant prices. Dividing the former set of values by the latter one yields the required price index.

In considering costs and returns, both have to be measured in pounds of the same year and it is most convenient to adjust the level of prices to accord with the costs and DE assumptions by using the general price index, shown above, to inflate the DR values. For example, if DR values in £ (76/77) are being used and DE values are in £ (78/79), the former should be multiplied by 123.63/100.0 or 1.236 to bring DR also into the same £ (78/79) terms.

Appendix 4

Tables of discounted revenue per hectare calculated to the year of planting (DR$_o$) for range of felling ages in £ (76/77) using the prices given in Appendix 2

Note: The figures in this Appendix are derived from Yield Models to be available 1981 which are slightly different from those in the Management Tables. The data have been smoothed and rounded. Figures in bold type are maximum values and accord with the optimum felling ages in Appendix 7.

$$\text{DR}_o \quad 3\%$$
Thin

Table 1 (a)   Conifers Thinned at Management Table Age of First Thinning, DR$_o$ at 3%

Scots Pine   *Felling Age*

YC	50	55	60	65	70	75	80	85	90	YC
4				85	105	115	120	**120**	120	4
6	125	175	215	245	260	270	**275**	270	265	6
8	310	375	425	455	470	**475**	475	465	450	8
10	555	630	680	710	**720**	720	710	695	675	10
12	845	920	970	995	**1,000**	995	980	955	930	12
14	1,155	1,240	1,285	**1,305**	1,305	1,290	1,270	1,245	1,210	14

Corsican Pine *Felling Age*

YC	35	40	45	50	55	60	65	70	75	YC
6	40	95	155	205	240	265	275	**275**	270	6
8	210	290	360	420	460	485	495	**495**	485	8
10	390	500	585	655	700	725	**735**	730	715	10
12	580	720	830	905	955	985	**990**	980	965	12
14	785	955	1,085	1,175	1,230	1,255	**1,255**	1,245	1,220	14
16	1,000	1,205	1,355	1,455	1,510	1,535	**1,535**	1,515	1,485	16
18	1,235	1,470	1,635	1,740	1,800	**1,820**	1,815	1,790	1,750	18
20	1,485	1,745	1,920	2,030	2,090	**2,105**	2,095	2,065	2,020	20

Lodgepole Pine *Felling Age*

YC	35	40	45	50	55	60	65	70	75	YC
4						80	95	105	**110**	4
6			160	205	230	250	260	265	**265**	6
8	190	285	355	405	435	455	470	**475**	470	8
10	390	500	585	640	680	705	720	**725**	720	10
12	615	745	840	910	955	980	995	**995**	990	12
14	850	1,005	1,120	1,195	1,245	1,275	**1,285**	1,280	1,270	14

49

Appendix 4 (continued)

Table 1 (a) continued

Sitka Spruce   *Felling Age*

YC	35	40	45	50	55	60	65	70	75	YC
6			170	215	255	275	285	**290**	280	6
8		260	350	420	470	495	**505**	500	490	8
10	320	455	570	660	720	745	**750**	735	720	10
12	515	685	825	920	980	**1,005**	1,000	980	960	12
14	735	945	1,100	1,205	1,260	**1,280**	1,270	1,240	1,210	14
16	990	1,230	1,395	1,500	1,555	**1,565**	1,545	1,510	1,470	16
18	1,265	1,530	1,705	1,805	1,850	**1,855**	1,830	1,785	1,740	18
20	1,560	1,845	2,020	2,115	**2,155**	2,145	2,115	2,065	2,015	20
22	1,870	2,165	2,340	2,425	**2,455**	2,440	2,400	2,350	2,290	22
24	2,190	2,485	2,650	2,730	**2,745**	2,725	2,685	2,630	2,570	24

Norway Spruce   *Felling Age*

YC	35	40	45	50	55	60	65	70	75	YC
6			65	115	155	185	210	225	**235**	6
8		140	215	285	340	380	410	425	**435**	8
10	185	295	400	490	565	615	645	655	**665**	10
12	335	490	630	740	825	880	905	915	**920**	12
14	525	725	890	1,020	1,110	1,165	1,190	**1,195**	1,190	14
16	740	980	1,170	1,315	1,410	1,465	**1,485**	1,485	1,475	16
18	980	1,255	1,470	1,620	1,720	1,775	**1,790**	1,780	1,765	18
20	1,225	1,540	1,770	1,930	2,025	2,075	**2,085**	2,075	2,055	20
22	1,470	1,830	2,075	2,230	2,320	2,365	**2,375**	2,370	2,345	22

Japanese Larch *Felling Age*

YC	35	40	45	50	55	60	65	70	75	YC
4	50	100	130	150	165	170	170	170	160	4
6	220	285	325	350	365	370	370	365	355	6
8	430	510	565	600	615	620	620	610	600	8
10	675	775	840	885	905	910	905	895	880	10
12	945	1,065	1,140	1,190	1,210	1,220	1,215	1,200	1,185	12
14	1,230	1,365	1,455	1,505	1,530	1,535	1,525	1,510	1,490	14

Douglas Fir *Felling Age*

YC	35	40	45	50	55	60	65	70	75	YC
8		300	400	470	515	545	565	565	555	8
10	390	545	660	745	800	830	835	825	810	10
12	625	805	935	1,025	1,080	1,105	1,110	1,090	1,070	12
14	870	1,075	1,220	1,310	1,365	1,385	1,380	1,360	1,335	14
16	1,130	1,355	1,505	1,600	1,650	1,665	1,655	1,635	1,600	16
18	1,400	1,645	1,800	1,895	1,940	1,950	1,940	1,910	1,875	18
20	1,675	1,935	2,100	2,190	2,230	2,240	2,225	2,195	2,155	20
22	1,960	2,235	2,405	2,495	2,530	2,535	2,520	2,490	2,445	22
24	2,250	2,535	2,710	2,800	2,835	2,840	2,825	2,795	2,745	24

Appendix 4 (continued)

DR₀ 5%
Thin

Table 1 (b) Conifers Thinned at Management Table Age of First Thinning, DR_0 at 5%

Scots Pine *Felling Age*

YC	35	40	45	50	55	60	65	70	75	YC
4						15	20	25	**25**	4
6				40	55	65	**65**	65	65	6
8		55	95	115	125	130	**135**	130	120	8
10	95	150	190	215	225	**230**	225	215	205	10
12	215	280	320	340	**350**	345	340	325	315	12
14	350	420	465	490	**495**	490	475	460	445	14

Corsican Pine *Felling Age*

YC	35	40	45	50	55	60	65	70	75	YC
6		65	80	85	**85**	80	75	70	65	6
8		140	165	170	**170**	165	160	155	140	8
10	195	235	260	270	**270**	265	255	245	230	10
12	305	345	370	**385**	380	375	360	345	330	12
14	415	470	495	**505**	500	490	470	450	430	14
16	535	600	630	**635**	630	610	590	565	545	16
18	660	735	770	**775**	760	740	715	685	660	18
20	800	880	910	**915**	900	870	840	810	780	20

Lodgepole Pine   *Felling Age*

YC	35	40	45	50	55	60	65	70	75	YC
4						25	**25**	25	25	4
6			65	75	**80**	80	75	70	65	6
8	95	135	150	**155**	155	155	150	145	135	8
10	200	235	255	**260**	260	255	245	235	225	10
12	320	360	380	**385**	380	370	360	345	335	12
14	445	490	510	**515**	505	495	480	465	450	14

Sitka Spruce   *Felling Age*

YC	35	40	45	50	55	60	65	70	75	YC
6			70	85	**90**	90	85	80	70	6
8		125	150	165	**175**	170	160	150	140	8
10	165	215	250	265	**270**	265	250	235	220	10
12	265	330	365	**385**	385	370	355	335	315	12
14	385	460	500	**510**	505	490	465	440	420	14
16	525	605	645	**650**	640	615	585	560	535	16
18	675	760	795	**800**	780	750	715	685	655	18
20	840	925	**960**	950	925	890	855	820	785	20
22	1,015	1,100	**1,125**	1,110	1,075	1,035	995	960	925	22
24	1,195	1,275	**1,295**	1,270	1,230	1,185	1,140	1,105	1,065	24

Appendix 4 (continued)

DR_o **5%** Thin

Table 1 (b) (continued)

Norway spruce

Felling Age

YC	35	40	45	50	55	60	65	70	75	YC
6			25	40	50	55	**55**	55	55	6
8		60	85	105	115	**120**	120	115	110	8
10	95	135	165	190	200	**205**	200	190	185	10
12	170	270	170	295	305	**305**	300	285	275	12
14	270	345	390	420	425	**425**	410	395	380	14
16	385	475	525	550	**560**	550	535	515	495	16
18	515	615	670	695	**700**	685	665	640	620	18
20	650	760	820	**840**	835	820	795	775	750	20
22	785	910	970	**985**	975	955	930	905	875	22

Japanese Larch

Felling Age

YC	35	40	45	50	55	60	65	70	75	YC
4	25	45	55	**55**	55	50	50	45	35	4
6	110	130	140	**140**	135	130	120	115	110	6
8	225	245	**255**	255	245	240	230	220	210	8
10	360	385	**395**	390	385	370	360	345	335	10
12	515	545	**550**	550	535	520	505	490	475	12
14	680	710	**720**	715	700	680	660	645	625	14

Douglas Fir *Felling Age*

YC	35	40	45	50	55	60	65	70	75	YC
8		140	175	190	**190**	190	185	175	165	8
10	205	260	295	310	**310**	305	290	280	265	10
12	330	390	425	**435**	435	420	405	385	370	12
14	460	530	560	**565**	560	545	520	500	480	14
16	600	670	700	**705**	690	670	645	620	595	16
18	750	820	**850**	845	825	800	775	745	720	18
20	900	975	**1,000**	995	970	940	910	880	850	20
22	1,060	1,140	**1,160**	1,145	1,120	1,085	1,050	1,020	990	22
24	1,225	1,305	**1,325**	1,305	1,275	1,240	1,205	1,170	1,135	24

Appendix 4 (*continued*)

Table 1 (c) Conifers Thinned at Management Table Age of First Thinning, DR_o at 7%

DR_o Thin 7%

Scots Pine *Felling Age*

YC	35	40	45	50	55	60	65	70	75	YC
4						5	**5**	5	5	4
6				15	20	**20**	15	15	15	6
8		25	40	**45**	40	40	40	35	30	8
10		70	80	**85**	85	80	75	70	65	10
12	45	135	140	**145**	140	130	125	115	110	12
14	185	210	**220**	215	210	200	190	180	175	14

Corsican Pine *Felling Age*

YC	25	30	35	40	45	50	55	60	65	YC
6			10	20	25	**30**	30	25	25	6
8		30	50	65	**70**	70	65	60	55	8
10	45	80	105	115	**120**	120	110	105	95	10
12	95	135	160	175	**175**	170	160	150	145	12
14	140	190	220	235	**240**	230	220	205	195	14
16	185	250	290	**305**	305	295	280	265	255	16
18	240	320	360	**380**	375	365	345	330	315	18
20	305	395	440	**455**	455	435	415	395	380	20

Lodgepole Pine *Felling Age*

YC	30	35	40	45	50	55	60	65	70	YC
4							**5**	5	5	4
6				**30**	30	30	25	20	20	6
8	30	50	60	**65**	65	60	55	50	45	8
10	75	105	**115**	115	110	105	95	90	85	10
12	140	170	**180**	175	170	160	150	140	135	12
14	210	235	**245**	240	230	220	210	200	190	14

Sitka Spruce *Felling Age*

YC	30	35	40	45	50	55	60	65	70	YC
6				30	**30**	30	30	25	20	6
8	25	50	65	65	**65**	65	60	55	50	8
10	60	90	105	**115**	110	105	100	90	85	10
12	105	145	160	**170**	165	155	145	135	125	12
14	165	205	230	**235**	230	215	200	185	175	14
16	235	280	305	**305**	295	280	265	245	235	16
18	315	365	**390**	385	375	350	330	315	300	18
20	405	460	**480**	475	455	430	405	385	370	20
22	505	560	**575**	565	540	510	485	465	450	22
24	615	670	**680**	660	630	600	570	550	530	24

Appendix 4 (continued)

Table 1 (c) (continued)

DR₀ **7**%
Thin

Norway Spruce *Felling Age*

YC	30	35	40	45	50	55	60	65	70	YC
6				10	15	**15**	15	15	15	6
8			30	35	**40**	35	35	35	30	8
10		50	65	70	**75**	75	70	65	60	10
12	55	90	110	120	**120**	120	110	105	100	12
14	100	145	165	175	**180**	170	165	155	145	14
16	160	205	230	**245**	240	235	220	210	200	16
18	220	275	305	**315**	310	300	285	270	260	18
20	285	350	380	**390**	385	370	350	335	325	20
22	350	425	465	**470**	460	440	420	400	390	22

Japanese Larch *Felling Age*

YC	25	30	35	40	45	50	55	60	65	YC
4			10	20	**20**	20	15	15	10	4
6		40	55	**60**	60	55	50	45	40	6
8	65	100	120	**120**	120	110	105	95	90	8
10	135	175	195	**200**	195	185	175	165	160	10
12	225	265	285	**290**	280	270	255	245	235	12
14	315	365	385	**390**	380	365	345	335	325	14

Douglas Fir *Felling Age*

YC	25	30	35	40	45	50	55	60	65	YC
8		25	50	65	75	**75**	75	70	65	8
10	40	80	110	125	**135**	135	130	120	110	10
12	90	140	175	195	**200**	195	185	170	160	12
14	140	205	245	265	**265**	260	245	230	220	14
16	200	280	325	**340**	340	325	310	290	280	16
18	265	360	405	**425**	415	400	380	360	345	18
20	335	445	495	**510**	500	475	455	435	415	20
22	415	535	590	**600**	585	560	535	510	495	22
24	505	630	685	**695**	680	650	620	595	575	24

Appendix 4 (continued)

Table 2 (a) Conifers—Non Thin, DR₀ at 3%

Scots Pine *Felling Age*

YC	45	50	55	60	65	70	75	80	85	YC
4			40	80	110	125	135	**140**	135	4
6	100	175	225	260	280	**285**	280	265	250	6
8	320	385	425	445	**445**	435	415	390	355	8
10	525	585	620	**625**	615	590	555	510	465	10
12	735	795	**815**	810	785	745	695	640	580	12
14	970	1,015	**1,020**	1,000	955	905	840	775	705	14

Corsican Pine *Felling Age*

YC	35	40	45	50	55	60	65	70	75	YC
6		130	190	235	265	275	**275**	265	250	6
8	230	325	390	425	**435**	435	415	390	360	8
10	420	515	570	**595**	595	580	545	505	460	10
12	600	695	745	**760**	745	715	670	615	560	12
14	775	870	**915**	915	890	845	790	725	650	14
16	940	1,040	**1,075**	1,070	1,030	975	905	830	745	16
18	1,100	1,200	**1,235**	1,220	1,175	1,105	1,025	935	845	18
20	1,260	1,360	**1,395**	1,375	1,320	1,245	1,150	1,045	945	20

Lodgepole Pine   *Felling Age*

YC	35	40	45	50	55	60	65	70	75	YC
4			35	80	105	120	130	135	**135**	4
6		170	225	260	275	**280**	280	270	255	6
8	275	355	405	430	**435**	425	410	385	360	8
10	450	540	580	**595**	585	565	535	500	465	10
12	645	725	**755**	755	740	705	665	620	570	12
14	840	905	**930**	920	890	850	800	745	690	14

Sitka Spruce   *Felling Age*

YC	35	40	45	50	55	60	65	70	75	YC
6		155	220	280	315	**330**	320	300	285	6
8	220	330	410	465	**490**	490	470	440	410	8
10	395	520	605	655	**670**	660	625	580	540	10
12	580	720	810	855	**860**	835	785	725	670	12
14	780	930	1,020	**1,060**	1,055	1,015	950	875	800	14
16	990	1,155	1,240	**1,270**	1,250	1,195	1,115	1,025	935	16
18	1,220	1,385	1,470	**1,485**	1,450	1,375	1,280	1,170	1,065	18
20	1,455	1,630	**1,705**	1,705	1,650	1,560	1,445	1,320	1,195	20
22	1,710	1,880	**1,945**	1,925	1,850	1,740	1,605	1,460	1,320	22
24	1,980	2,145	**2,190**	2,150	2,055	1,920	1,760	1,600	1,440	24

Appendix 4 (continued)

Table 2 (a)   continued

Norway Spruce   *Felling Age*

YC	35	40	45	50	55	60	65	70	75	YC
6		15	110	175	215	245	270	**280**	270	6
8		200	295	365	410	440	**445**	435	425	8
10	250	390	495	565	610	**625**	625	605	575	10
12	430	590	705	775	815	**820**	800	765	720	12
14	625	800	920	995	**1,020**	1,010	975	920	860	14
16	830	1,020	1,145	1,210	**1,225**	1,205	1,145	1,075	995	16
18	1,040	1,240	1,370	1,430	**1,430**	1,390	1,315	1,220	1,125	18
20	1,250	1,470	1,595	**1,645**	1,630	1,570	1,475	1,365	1,250	20
22	1,460	1,700	1,825	**1,855**	1,820	1,735	1,630	1,500	1,365	22

Japanese Larch   *Felling Age*

YC	30	35	40	45	50	55	60	65	70	YC
4		90	145	175	190	**195**	195	190	180	4
6	195	280	330	360	**365**	360	340	320	295	6
8	375	470	525	**545**	540	520	495	460	425	8
10	575	670	720	**735**	720	690	650	605	555	10
12	780	875	920	**930**	905	865	810	750	685	12
14	975	1,080	**1,130**	1,130	1,095	1,040	970	890	810	14

Douglas Fir   *Felling Age*

YC	30	35	40	45	50	55	60	65	70	YC
8	90	215	320	405	460	490	**495**	480	455	8
10	260	420	540	625	675	**695**	685	655	615	10
12	445	630	765	850	890	**895**	865	815	760	12
14	640	855	995	1,075	**1,105**	1,085	1,040	970	895	14
16	845	1,080	1,225	1,295	**1,310**	1,275	1,205	1,115	1,015	16
18	1,060	1,305	1,455	**1,515**	1,520	1,455	1,365	1,255	1,135	18
20	1,275	1,535	1,680	**1,730**	1,705	1,630	1,515	1,380	1,245	20
22	1,490	1,765	1,905	**1,940**	1,895	1,780	1,650	1,500	1,360	22
24	1,700	1,985	2,125	**2,140**	2,070	1,940	1,780	1,615	1,470	24

Appendix 4 (continued)

Table 2 (b) Conifers—Non Thin, DR$_0$ at 5%

Scots Pine *Felling Age*

YC	35	40	45	50	55	60	65	70	75	YC
4					15	25	30	**35**	30	4
6			45	65	80	**85**	80	75	65	6
8	50	100	135	145	**145**	140	130	115	100	8
10	155	200	220	**225**	215	195	175	155	130	10
12	245	295	**310**	305	285	255	225	195	165	12
14	380	**410**	410	390	355	315	275	235	200	14

Corsican Pine *Felling Age*

YC	35	40	45	50	55	60	65	70	75	YC
6	25	60	80	90	**90**	85	80	70	60	6
8	120	150	**165**	160	150	135	120	100	85	8
10	215	240	**240**	230	205	180	155	130	110	10
12	305	**325**	315	290	260	225	190	160	130	12
14	395	**405**	385	350	310	265	225	190	155	14
16	480	**480**	460	410	360	305	260	215	175	16
18	**560**	555	520	470	405	350	295	245	200	18
20	**640**	630	590	525	460	390	330	275	225	20

Lodgepole Pine *Felling Age*

YC	35	40	45	50	55	60	65	70	75	YC
4			15	30	35	**40**	35	35	30	4
6		80	95	**100**	95	85	80	70	60	6
8	140	165	**170**	165	150	135	115	100	85	8
10	230	**250**	245	230	205	180	155	130	110	10
12	330	**335**	320	290	255	220	190	160	135	12
14	**430**	420	390	350	310	265	230	195	165	14

Sitka Spruce *Felling Age*

YC	35	40	45	50	55	60	65	70	75	YC
6	115	70	95	105	**110**	105	90	80	65	6
8	200	155	175	**180**	170	155	135	115	95	8
10	295	240	**255**	250	235	210	180	150	125	10
12	395	335	**340**	325	405	265	225	190	160	12
14	505	430	**430**	405	365	320	270	230	190	14
16	620	**535**	525	485	435	375	320	270	220	16
18	740	**640**	620	570	500	435	365	305	250	18
20	870	**755**	720	650	570	490	415	345	280	20
22	**870**	870	820	735	640	545	460	380	310	22
24	**1,005**	990	925	825	715	605	505	415	340	24

Appendix 4 (continued)

DR₀ NT **5%**

Table 2 (b) (continued)

Norway Spruce Felling Age

YC	35	40	45	50	55	60	65	70	75	YC
6		10	45	65	75	**80**	75	70	65	6
8		95	125	140	**145**	140	125	115	100	8
10	125	180	210	**215**	215	200	175	155	135	10
12	220	270	295	**300**	285	260	230	195	170	12
14	320	370	**385**	380	355	320	280	240	205	14
16	425	470	**480**	465	430	380	325	275	235	16
18	530	570	**575**	550	500	440	375	315	270	18
20	640	**675**	670	630	570	495	420	350	300	20
22	750	**780**	765	710	640	550	460	385	330	22

Japanese Larch Felling Age

YC	35	40	45	50	55	60	65	70	75	YC
4	45	65	**75**	75	70	60	55	50	40	4
6	140	**155**	150	140	125	105	90	80	65	6
8	240	**245**	230	205	180	155	130	110	90	8
10	**345**	335	310	275	240	205	175	145	120	10
12	**445**	425	390	345	300	255	215	180	145	12
14	**550**	525	475	420	360	305	255	210	175	14

66

Douglas Fir *Felling Age*

YC	35	40	45	50	55	60	65	70	75	YC
8	110	150	170	**175**	170	155	140	120	105	8
10	215	250	**265**	260	240	215	190	160	130	10
12	320	355	**360**	340	310	275	235	195	160	12
14	435	**460**	455	420	375	325	280	235	190	14
16	550	**570**	545	500	440	380	320	265	220	16
18	665	**675**	640	580	505	430	360	300	245	18
20	**780**	780	730	650	565	475	395	325	265	20
22	**900**	885	820	725	620	520	430	350	275	22
24	**1,015**	990	905	790	670	560	465	375	275	24

67

Appendix 4 (continued)

Table 2 (c) Conifers—Non Thin, DR₀ at 7%

Scots Pine *Felling Age*

YC	30	35	40	45	50	55	60	65	70	YC
4						5	10	10	10	4
6				20	25	30	25	25	20	6
8		25	45	55	55	50	40	35	30	8
10	80	95	95	90	80	70	60	45	35	10
12	90	125	135	130	115	95	75	60	50	12
14	175	195	195	175	150	125	100	80	65	14

Corsican Pine *Felling Age*

YC	25	30	35	40	45	50	55	60	65	YC
6			10	30	35	35	30	30	25	6
8		35	60	70	70	65	55	45	35	8
10	50	90	110	110	105	90	75	60	45	10
12	105	145	155	150	135	115	90	70	55	12
14	150	195	205	190	165	135	110	85	65	14
16	200	245	245	225	195	160	125	100	75	16
18	250	290	290	265	225	180	145	110	85	18
20	310	340	335	300	250	205	160	125	100	20

Lodgepole Pine *Felling Age*

YC	25	30	35	40	45	50	55	60	65	YC
4					5	10	**15**	10	10	4
6				40	**40**	**40**	35	30	25	6
8		45	75	**80**	75	65	55	45	35	8
10	50	100	**120**	120	105	90	70	55	45	10
12	115	160	**170**	160	135	110	90	70	55	12
14	180	**220**	220	200	170	135	110	85	70	14

Sitka Spruce *Felling Age*

YC	25	30	35	40	45	50	55	60	65	YC
6				35	40	**40**	40	35	25	6
8		25	60	70	**75**	70	60	50	40	8
10		75	105	**115**	110	100	85	65	50	10
12	70	125	150	**155**	145	130	105	85	65	12
14	115	180	**205**	205	185	160	130	100	80	14
16	175	240	**260**	250	225	190	155	120	95	16
18	245	305	**320**	300	265	220	180	140	110	18
20	320	375	**380**	355	310	255	200	155	120	20
22	400	**455**	450	410	350	290	225	175	135	22
24	490	**535**	520	465	395	320	250	195	150	24

Appendix 4 (continued)

DR₀
NT **7%**

Table 2 (c) (continued)

Norway Spruce *Felling Age*

YC	30	35	40	45	50	55	60	65	70	YC
6			5	15	25	**30**	25	20	20	6
8			45	50	**55**	50	45	35	30	8
10		65	85	**90**	85	75	65	50	40	10
12	70	110	**130**	125	115	100	85	65	55	12
14	125	165	**175**	165	150	125	100	80	65	14
16	180	215	**220**	205	180	150	120	95	75	16
18	240	**270**	270	250	215	175	140	110	85	18
20	300	**330**	320	290	245	200	160	125	95	20
22	360	**385**	370	330	280	225	175	135	105	22

Japanese Larch *Felling Age*

YC	20	25	30	35	40	45	50	55	60	YC
4				25	**30**	**30**	30	25	20	4
6			60	**75**	75	65	55	45	35	6
8		85	120	**125**	115	100	80	65	50	8
10	85	155	**180**	175	160	135	105	85	65	10
12	160	230	**250**	230	200	165	135	105	80	12
14	235	300	**310**	290	245	200	160	130	100	14

Douglas Fir *Felling Age*

YC	25	30	35	40	45	50	55	60	65	YC
8		30	55	70	**75**	70	60	50	40	8
10	40	85	110	**115**	115	100	85	70	55	10
12	90	140	165	**165**	155	135	110	85	70	12
14	150	205	**220**	215	195	165	135	105	80	14
16	210	270	**280**	265	235	195	155	120	95	16
18	275	335	**345**	320	275	225	180	140	105	18
20	340	405	**405**	370	315	255	200	155	120	20
22	410	**470**	465	415	350	280	220	165	130	22
24	485	**535**	520	465	390	310	235	180	135	24

Appendix 5

Tables of Discounted Volumes

Table 1 Volumes per Hectare Discounted to Year 0 (DV$_0$) for Crops First Thinned at Management Table Age (see Appendix 8)

(a) DV$_0$ at 3%

DV$_0$ Thin 3%

Yield Class	SP	CP	LP	SS	NS	JL	DF	Yield Class
4	33		36					4
6	58	61	62	60	54	45		6
8	85	88	90	87	80	72	87	8
10	114	117	120	114	107	100	115	10
12	145	146	151	142	135	129	144	12
14	177	175	183	170	164	160	174	14
16		204		199	193	192	204	16
18		234		228	222		234	18
20		264		257	251		264	20
22				286	281		294	22
24				315			324	24

DV$_0$ Thin 5%

(b) DV$_0$ at 5%

Yield Class	SP	CP	LP	SS	NS	JL	DF	Yield Class
4	10		13			19		4
6	21	24	25	23	18	34		6
8	33	37	39	35	30	50	36	8
10	46	51	54	48	42	66	50	10
12	60	66	71	62	54	85	65	12
14	75	82	88	77	67	102	81	14
16		98		92	81		97	16
18		115		108	96		113	18
20		132		125	112		129	20
22				142	129		145	22
24				159			163	24

Appendix 5 (*continued*)

Table 1 (continued)

(c) DV$_0$ at 7%

DV$_0$ **7%**
Thin

Yield Class	SP	CP	LP	SS	NS	JL	DF	Yield Class
4	4							4
6	9	10	5	10	8	10		6
8	15	18	12	16	14	18	16	8
10	22	26	20	23	20	28	24	10
12	30	34	29	31	26	38	32	12
14	39	43	39	39	33	49	41	14
16		52	50	48	41	61	51	16
18		62		58	49		61	18
20		72		68	58		72	20
22				79	68		83	22
24				90			94	24

Appendix 5 (continued)

DV_0 **3%**
NT

Table 2 Volumes per Hectare Discounted to Year 0 (DV_0) for Crops to be Left Unthinned

(a) DV_0 at 3%

Yield Class	SP	CP	LP	SS	NS	JL	DF	Yield Class
4	24		28			35		4
6	41	48	49	50	41	54		6
8	58	67	69	68	59	72	66	8
10	74	85	88	86	77	89	84	10
12	90	102	106	104	95	105	101	12
14	106	118	123	122	112	120	118	14
16		134		140	129		135	16
18		149		158	146		152	18
20		163		176	163		169	20
22				196	180		186	22
24				216			203	24

Appendix 5 (*continued*)

Table 2 (continued)
(b) DV$_o$ at 5%

DV$_o$ 5%
NT

Yield Class	SP	CP	LP	SS	NS	JL	DF	Yield Class
4	7		9			16		4
6	14	19	19	18	14	26		6
8	22	28	29	27	22	36	27	8
10	31	37	39	36	31	46	36	10
12	41	47	49	45	40	56	46	12
14	52	57	60	55	49	66	56	14
16		67		64	58		66	16
18		77		73	67		76	18
20		87		83	76		86	20
22				92	85		96	22
24				101			106	24

(c) DV_0 at 7%

Yield Class	SP	CP	LP	SS	NS	JL	DF	Yield Class
4	3		4					4
6	6	8	10	8	6	7		6
8	10	14	16	13	10	14	13	8
10	15	20	22	18	14	21	19	10
12	21	26	29	23	19	28	25	12
14	28	32	36	29	24	35	31	14
16		38		35	29	42	37	16
18		44		41	35		43	18
20		50		48	41		49	20
22				55	47		55	22
24				62			61	24

Appendix 5 (*continued*)

Table 3 Volumes per Hectare Discounted to Management Table Age[a] (DV$_t$) of First Thinning
for All[b] Thinned Conifer Crops

$$DV_t \text{ Thin } 3, 5 \text{ \& } 7\%$$

Yield Class	3%	5%	7%	Yield Class
4	115	80	70	4
6	160	110	90	6
8	200	140	110	8
10	240	170	135	10
12	280	195	155	12
14	325	225	175	14
16	365	255	200	16
18	405	280	220	18
20	445	310	240	20
22	485	340	265	22
24	530	370	285	24

Notes: (a) Management Table ages of first thinning are given in Appendix 8.
(b) For JL use figures 10 per cent lower than shown at 3%, 5% and 7%, for NS YC16 and above add 5 per cent to the figures shown at 3% only.

78

Table 4 Final Felling Volume (FV) for Unthinned Crops
Felled at the Age of Maximum DR (see Appendix 7)

FV
NT **3**%

(a) Volumes at age of max DR at 3%

Yield Class	SP	CP	LP	SS	NS	JL	DF	Yield Class
4	255		250			185		4
6	315	300	295	295	330	235		6
8	370	350	340	365	405	285	380	8
10	420	400	385	435	475	335	430	10
12	465	445	430	495	540	385	480	12
14	505	490	475	555	600	435	530	14
16		535		605	655		570	16
18		580		655	705		610	18
20		625		705	750		650	20
22				755	790		690	22
24				805			730	24

Appendix 5 (continued)

FV
NT **5%**

Table 4 (continued)
(b) Volumes at age of max DR at 5%

Yield Class	SP	CP	LP	SS	NS	JL	DF	Yield Class
4	215		190			160		4
6	250	250	220	260	270	195		6
8	290	290	255	300	315	230	310	8
10	325	320	285	340	360	265	345	10
12	365	355	320	380	400	300	380	12
14	405	390	350	420	445	335	420	14
16		425		460	490		455	16
18		450		500	530		490	18
20		485		535	575		525	20
22				575	620		565	22
24				615			590	24

(c) Volumes at age of max DR at 7%

Yield Class	SP	CP	LP	SS	NS	JL	DF	Yield Class
4	210		170			140		4
6	230	215	205	220	230	175		6
8	250	245	240	255	265	210	265	8
10	270	275	270	290	300	240	295	10
12	300	305	300	325	335	270	325	12
14	330	335	330	360	370	300	355	14
16		360		390	400		385	16
18		385		420	430		415	18
20		410		450	460		445	20
22				480	490		475	22
24				510			500	24

81

Appendix 6

Discounted Revenue per hectare for different thinning regimes in Sitka Spruce

Values in £(76/77) using the prices given in Appendix 2 and compounded forward to the Management Table Time (MTT) of first thinning (DR$_t$)

Yield class	MTT of 1st thinning (yrs)	DR$_t$ at 3%				DR$_t$ at 5%				DR$_t$ at 7%			
		MTT	Delay 5 yrs	Delay 10 yrs	Non-thin	MTT	Delay 5 yrs	Delay 10 yrs	Non-thin MTT	MTT	Delay 5 yrs	Delay 10 yrs	Non-thin
8	29	1,185	1,280	1,300	1,165	700	795	805	745	480	560	565	545
10	26	1,610	1,685	1,700	1,445	960	1,040	1,040	915	655	730	715	660
12	24	2,040	2,100	2,105	1,740	1,230	1,295	1,280	1,090	845	910	875	785
14	22	2,470	2,515	2,505	2,040	1,510	1,560	1,530	1,280	1,050	1,100	1,045	925
16	21	2,900	2,935	2,910	2,350	1,805	1,835	1,785	1,480	1,270	1,300	1,225	1,075
18	20	3,335	3,360	3,315	2,675	2,105	2,120	2,050	1,695	1,500	1,510	1,405	1,235
20	19	3,770	3,790	3,720	3,010	2,420	2,415	2,315	1,920	1,745	1,730	1,600	1,405
22	18	4,210	4,225	4,130	3,350	2,745	2,725	2,590	2,155	2,005	1,960	1,800	1,590
24	18	4,650	4,665	4,540	3,705	3,080	3,040	2,870	2,405	2,275	2,200	2,010	1,780

Note: These figures differ slightly from the DR$_0$ figures in Appendix 4 compounded forward to MTT because the above data have been smoothed across yield classes after being compounded.

Appendix 7

Optimum Felling Ages (FA)
Ages of maximum DR using prices given in Appendix 2

FA Thin 3%

Ages of maximum DR using prices given in Appendix 2
Table 1 Thinned Stands—First Thinned at Management Table Age (see Appendix 8)

(a) Optimum felling ages at 3%—thin

Yield Class	SP	CP	LP	SS	NS	JL	DF	Yield Class
4	85		75			65		4
6	80	70	75	70	75	60		6
8	75	70	70	65	75	60	70	8
10	70	65	70	65	75	60	65	10
12	70	65	70	60	75	60	65	12
14	65	65	65	60	70	60	60	14
16		65		60	65		60	16
18		60		60	65		60	18
20		60		55	65		60	20
22				55	65		60	22
24				55			60	24

(b) Optimum felling ages at 5%—thin

Yield Class	SP	CP	LP	SS	NS	JL	DF	Yield Class
4	75		65					4
6	65	55	55	55	65	50		6
8	65	55	50	55	60	50	55	8
10	60	55	50	55	60	45	55	10
12	55	50	50	55	55	45	50	12
14	55	50	50	50	55	45	50	14
16		50		50	55	45	50	16
18		50		50	55		45	18
20		50		45	50		45	20
22				45	50		45	22
24				45			45	24

85

Appendix 7 (*continued*)

Table 1 (continued)
(c) Optimum felling ages at 7%—thin

FA
Thin 7%

Yield Class	SP	CP	LP	SS	NS	JL	DF	Yield Class
4	65		60			45		4
6	60	50	45	50	55	40		6
8	50	45	45	50	50	40	50	8
10	50	45	40	45	50	40	45	10
12	50	45	40	45	50	40	45	12
14	45	45	40	45	50	40	45	14
16		40		45	45		40	16
18		40		40	45		40	18
20		40		40	45		40	20
22				40	45		40	22
24				40			40	24

Table 2 Non Thin Stands

(a) Optimum felling ages at 3%—non-thin

Yield Class	SP	CP	LP	SS	NS	JL	DF	Yield Class
4	80		75					4
6	70	65	60	60	70	55		6
8	65	55	55	55	65	50	60	8
10	60	55	50	55	60	45	55	10
12	55	50	45	55	60	45	55	12
14	55	50	45	50	55	45	50	14
16		45		50	55	40	50	16
18		45		50	55		45	18
20		45		45	50		45	20
22				45	50		45	22
24				45			45	24

Appendix 7 (continued)

Table 2 (continued)

(b) Optimum felling ages at 5%—non-thin

FA
NT **5%**

Yield Class	SP	CP	LP	SS	NS	JL	DF	Yield Class
4	70		60			45		4
6	60	55	50	55	60	40		6
8	55	45	45	50	55	40	50	8
10	50	45	40	45	50	35	45	10
12	45	40	40	45	50	35	45	12
14	40	40	35	40	45	35	40	14
16		40		40	45		40	16
18		35		40	45		40	18
20		35		40	40		35	20
22				35	40		35	22
24				35			35	24

(c) Optimum felling ages at 7%—non-thin

Yield Class	SP	CP	LP	SS	NS	JL	DF	Yield Class
4	65		55			40		4
6	55	50	45	50	55	35		6
8	50	40	40	45	50	35	45	8
10	40	40	35	40	45	30	40	10
12	40	35	35	40	40	30	40	12
14	35	35	30	35	40	30	35	14
16		35		35	40		35	16
18		30		35	35		35	18
20		30		35	35		35	20
22				30	35		30	22
24				30			30	24

Appendix 8

Age of first thinning as specified in the management tables

Species	Yield Classes											
	4	6	8	10	12	14	16	18	20	22	24
Scots pine	40	33	29	25	23	21	—	—	—	—	—
Corsican pine	—	33	28	25	23	21	20	19	18	—	—
Lodgepole pine	40	31	26	23	21	19	—	—	—	—	18
Sitka spruce	—	33	29	26	24	22	21	20	19	18	18
Norway spruce	—	35	31	28	26	24	23	22	21	20	—
Japanese/Hybird larch	26	22	19	17	15	14	—	—	—	—	—
Douglas fir	—	—	—	25	23	21	19	18	17	17	16

Note: These ages are based on a mensurational criterion and for economic (see section on thinning) or other management reasons, other, usually later, ages may be adopted.